AN INTROD
COMPUTER CO

OTHER TITLES OF INTEREST

AN INTRODUCTION TO COMPUTER COMMUNICATIONS

by
R. A. PENFOLD

BERNARD BABANI (publishing) LTD
THE GRAMPIANS
SHEPHERDS BUSH ROAD
LONDON W6 7NF
ENGLAND

PLEASE NOTE

Although every care has been taken with the production of this book to ensure that any projects, designs, modifications and/or programs etc. contained herewith, operate in a correct and safe manner and also that any components specified are normally available in Great Britain, the Publishers do not accept responsibility in any way for the failure, including fault in design, of any project, design, modification or program to work correctly or to cause damage to any other equipment that it may be connected to or used in conjunction with, or in respect of any other damage or injury that may be so caused, nor do the Publishers accept responsibility in any way for the failure to obtain specified components.

Notice is also given that if equipment that is still under warranty is modified in any way or used or connected with home-built equipment then that warranty may be void.

First Published – March 1986

British Library Cataloguing in Publication Data
Penfold, R.A.
   An introduction to computer communications.
   1. Computer networks
   I. Title
   004.6   TK5105.5

ISBN 0 85934 151 8

Printed and Bound in Great Britain by Cox & Wyman Ltd, Reading

Preface

Home computers have now become an everyday part of life for a great many people, and although they are not yet as commonplace as television sets and radios, the gap is closing. Probably the vast majority of home computers are underutilized, being used only for playing games in most cases. However, there seems to be a steady trend towards using home computers in a greater variety of applications, and communications seem to be the major growth area. For most users this means connecting the computer to the telephone system via a modem, and this opens up the possibility of computer communications between fellow enthusiasts, or the alternative chosen by most people, which is to access databases and similar systems. There are literally hundreds of thousands of pages of information available on a vast range of subjects, and other services such as ordering by computer are also available. Although this is the most relevant form of computer communications for most users, there are other types, such as local networking, or for the more adventurous, computer communications via radio.

For the newcomer to this aspect of computing there is a lot of technical jargon to overcome. The purpose of this book is to explain the basic principles and the practicalities of computer communications, assuming no prior knowledge other than that the reader has had a certain amount of practical experience with home computers, and is familiar with the main terminology. Three chapters cover modems, local networks, and radio links.

R. A. Penfold

CONTENTS

Chapter 1

MODEMS

Computer communications can be over distances ranging from a matter of inches to many thousands of miles, but probably most home computer users are interested in long distance communication over typically a range of something in the region of a few hundred miles. This can either be to enable two users to communicate with one another, possibly with a view to swopping programs, or the user can communicate with something like a large database or an electronic mail order system. In either case the ordinary telephone system can be used to carry the signals, but, unfortunately, connecting ordinary computer interfaces direct to the telephone system is not permissible, and would be unlikely to work anyway.

The problem is simply that the telephone system is only designed to handle audio frequency signals, and only the part of the audio range needed for good voice communications at that. Apart from any difficulties with incorrect signal levels (which could easily be corrected) signal waveforms would tend to be distorted to a degree that would prevent the system from operating at all. The only type of interface that might function via the telephone lines is a cassette type, but there are problems here as well. There are strict regulations regarding the frequencies that can be fed into the telephone system, and in order to come within these any normal cassette interface would require some signal conditioning to filter offending frequencies from the signal fed into the system. It might then be necessary to have further signal conditioning at the receiving end in order to reinstate the missing frequencies.

Although computer enthusiasts have been known to communicate via the telephone system using cassette interfaces this is not a way that is practical for general use. Apart from practical problems with connecting the interfaces to the telephone system legally, a cassette interface has the disadvantage of only providing communications in one direction at a time, or "half duplex" operation as this is known. As we shall see later, there are advantages to having simultaneous communications in both directions, or "full duplex" operation as this is termed. This can be provided using a device known as a "Modem" (MODulator/ DEModulator), which is actually rather like a somewhat refined cassette interface in the way it operates. The modem connects to a serial port of the RS232C or RS423 type, which are fitted to some home computers, and are available as some sort of add-on for many others. In fact some modems have a built-in interface which enables them to connect direct to the expansion port or cartridge port of a computer which does not have a serial interface.

It is by no means essential to have an understanding of how a modem functions in order to use one, and for several computers there are excellent modem packages available which enable the user to connect everything up and operate the system as easily as using a printer or some other relatively mundane peripheral device. However, as with practically any aspect of a technical subject such as home computing, the greater your understanding of the subject the better your chances of being able to fully utilize the equipment. Also, it leaves you in a position where you are better equipped to deal with any problems that arise or avoid any pitfalls into which you might otherwise stumble. You may prefer to skip over this section dealing with the basic way in which serial data systems and modems function, but it does explain some of the technical terms which you will inevitable encounter when dealing with modems, and it would be advisable to at least quickly read it through.

Serial Data
In order to understand how a modem functions it is first necessary to understand the basics of serial data. The computer normally handles data internally in parallel form, and some computer interfaces (the Centronics printer type for example) also handle data in this form. There are eight lines which carry the signals (or sixteen in some of the more recent and up-market machines), and these can each take up one of two signal levels, These are "high" (logic 1 or about 5 volts) and "low" (logic 0 or about 0 volts). We will only consider eight line systems here since normal serial systems only deal with eight bit bytes of data. With 8 lines and each one representing a binary digit, this gives a binary number

range of 00000000 to 11111111, or 0 to 255 in decimal. Even if you are not familiar with the binary numbering system, it should be apparent that with eight lines and each one having two possible states there are a total of 256 different combinations which the lines can adopt. In this case we are not really interested in numbers and the mathematics of the binary system, and all you really need to know is that each combination of output states represents a letter or some other keyboard characcter. In fact many of the code numbers are unused, particularly those from 128 to 255, as the letters of the alpbabet (in upper and lower case) plus numbers and other symbols only require about one hundred codes.

The nearest thing to a standard set of character codes is the ASCII set. ASCII stands for American Standard Code for Information Interchange, and most home computers use a set of codes which is closely based on this. In most cases characters such as letters and numbers have the same code numbers as in the standard ASCII set, but most home computers assign the spare code numbers to graphics characters. If you refer to the manual for your computer it will almost certainly give a complete list of the character codes it uses, and will probably mention whether or not they adhere closely to the ASCII set. A list of the main ASCII codes is given in the following list, and might help to clear up any doubts about the codes used by your computer.

A computer that does not use standard ASCII codes for the main characters is still usable in communications applications, but software must be used to convert both incoming and outgoing characters to ASCII codes. This can be done quite easily using the "look-up table" system.

So far we have seen how alphanumeric characters can be represented by a set of eight bit code numbers, which can in turn be represented by the logic levels present on eight electrical lines, but an eight wire (plus earth wire) system is not very convenient for long distance communications. Apart from the relatively high cost of the connecting cable, parallel systems generally fail to operate over distances of more than a few metres due to stray coupling causing signals on one wire breaking through onto others and corrupting the data. Also, as far as communications via the telephone system is concerned, the use of a two-wire system makes parallel data transfer an impossibility.

ASCII No	Character	ASCII No	Character	ASCII No	Character
27	ESC	32	Space	34	"
35	£ or #	36	$	37	%
38	&	39	'	40	(
41	)	42	*	43	+
44	,	45	–	46	.
47	/	48	0	49	1
50	2	51	3	52	4
53	5	54	6	55	7
56	8	57	9	58	:
59	;	61	=	63	?
64	@	65	A	66	B
67	C	68	D	69	E
70	F	71	G	72	H
73	I	74	J	75	K
76	L	77	M	78	N
79	O	80	P	81	Q
82	R	83	S	84	T
85	U	86	V	87	W
88	X	89	Y	90	Z
97	a	98	b	99	c
100	d	101	e	102	f
103	g	104	h	105	i
106	j	107	k	108	l
109	m	110	n	111	o
112	p	113	q	114	r
115	s	116	t	117	u
118	v	119	w	120	x
121	y	122	z	127	Del

There are actually two basic types of serial data system, synchronous and asynchronous, but the synchronous type requires a third line to provide a timing signal and is not applicable to telephone communications systems. In fact synchronous systems seem to be little used in practice. With an asynchronous system the timing signals must be placed onto the signal line together with the data. The data itself is sent one bit at a time with the least significant bit being transmitted first, running in sequence through to the most significant bit. If the binary code to be transmitted was 11100001, the line would first be set to logic 1 for one unit of time, then to logic 0 for four units of time, and then to logic 1 for three units of time. By sampling the single data line at appropriate intervals the receiving equipment can determine the state of each bit.

There are no real problems with cross coupling in serial data systems where there is only one signal lead, and other problems that can occur in parallel systems, such as unequal delays on the data lines, are also irrelevant. Any delays in the system will affect all bits equally, and will not scramble the data. Serial systems are not without their disadvantages though, and one is simply that the hardware is generally somewhat more complex and expensive. Data transfer using a serial system is also relatively slow, although still more than adequate for most purposes. However, be warned that it can take fifteen minutes or more to send or receive a long program via a modem. With an asynchronous system bytes of data can be sent in a more or less random fashion. For the system to be workable though, there has to be an additional bit sent at the beginning of each byte to tell the receiving equipment that 8 bits of data are about to be sent. This, as one would expect, is called the start bit. Practical serial interfaces such as the RS232C and RS423 types do not use ordinary logic voltage levels of 0 and +5 volts. With the RS232C system a positive voltage (about +12 volts) is used to indicate a logic 1, and a negative voltage (about −12 volts) is used to indicate a logic 0. With the RS423 system the signal voltages are somewhat lower than this at about plus and minus 5 volts, but this is within the minimum requirement (plus and minus 3 volts) of the RS232C system. A modem with an RS232C input should therefore function equally well if it is driven from an RS423 port.

The start bit is not the only additional bit that is transmitted along with the data bits, and there is also 1, 1.5, or 2 stop bits. These are not actually essential, and their main purpose is to give a simple form of error checking. If noise on the data line is causing problems, or if the receiving equipment has failed to detect the start bit properly, it is quite likely that the data line will be at the wrong level when a check for the presence of the stop bit or bits is made. The stop bit or bits also effectively ensure that there is a reasonable gap between one byte and the next, thus avoiding problems with one byte running straight on from the previous one, making it difficult for the receiving equipment to properly "frame" each byte.

Another form of error checking is the parity system. With this system every byte of data has either an odd or an even number of bits set to logic 1, depending on whether odd or even parity is used. Some additional electronics at the transmitting equipment is used to add an extra bit at the end of data blocks, where necessary, to ensure that either an odd or an even number of bits is always transmitted. A simple checking circuit at the receiving equipment can then check that each block of data contains a suitable number of logic 1s. If the data is corrupted it is quite likely that the number of bits at logic 1 will be odd when it should be even, or vice versa, but this system of checking is not totally reliable, and a double glitch could leave the parity unaffected. Parity error checking seems to be little used in practice, and I have not encountered it when using modems.

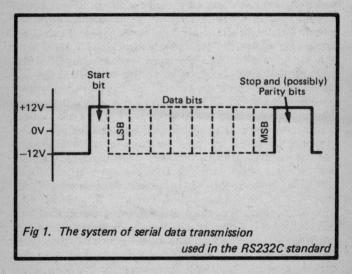

Fig 1. The system of serial data transmission
used in the RS232C standard

The diagram of Figure 1 shows how serial data is transmitted, and this might help to clarify the system for you. A point to note is that eight data bits are shown in Figure 1, but in practice anything from 5 to 8 data bits can be used. In a computer application only 7 and 8 data bits are normally used, since at least 7 data bits are required in order to handle ASCII and ASCII based codes. The most popular word format for use with modems seems to be one start bit, eight data bits, one stop bit, and no parity.

Baud Rate

The baud rate is merely the number of bits transmitted per second if a continuous stream of data is sent. There are a number of standard rates, and these are 75, 150, 300, 600, 1200, 1800, 2400, 4800, 9600, and 19200. Most modems transmit and receive at 300 baud, or transmit at 75 baud and receive at 1200 baud. The higher baud rates are unusable via the telephone system. In order to transfer data successfully it is essential for the transmitting and receiving baud rates to be the same. It is also unlikely that data will be transfered properly unless the word formats are also the same (i.e. the number of stop and data bits must be the same, as well as the type of parity if it is used). However, it is sometimes possible to get away with using the wrong word format if your equipment can not be set up for the correct one, and two stop bits instead of one often gives perfectly good results. There is no danger of damaging anything if you use the wrong word format, so it is worth a try. Incidentally, the number of start bits is often unspecified, but with the RS232C and RS423 systems there is always just one start bit.

When using modems it is important to realise that they are designed for a specific baud rate or rates, and a proper data transfer may not be obtained if the wrong rate is used, even if the computers at each end of the system are set up for the same baud rate and word format. In particular, do not try to use a higher baud rate than the one for which the modem is designed, as this is unlikely to give good reliablity in the unlikely event that it works at all.

Figure 2 gives details of the standard RS232C connections, but it has to be pointed out that most home computers fitted with a serial interface do not use the standard 25 way D connector illustrated in Figure 2. However, the manual for your computer should give connection details for its serial port if it is equipped with one. Even though some of the terminals of the 25 way connector are unused, a full RS232C interface has a fair number of functioning terminals. In practice most RS232C interfaces only implement five of these, and for use with a modem only three are needed. These are simply the earth, data input, and data output terminals. Most serial ports implement some "handshake" lines, which enable the receiving device to hold-off data if it is being

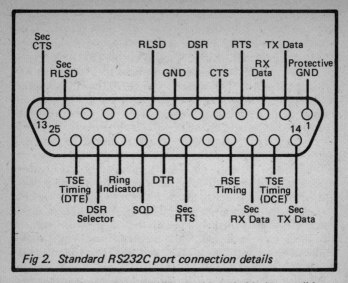

Fig 2. Standard RS232C port connection details

supplied at an excessive rate. It would probably be possible to device a system that implemented handshaking via the telephone wires, with the handshaking and data signals being multiplexed onto the same line at the transmitter, and then demultiplexed back to onto separate lines at the receiver. I do not know of a practical system of this type though, and it would really be an unnecessary complication anyway. The fairly slow baud rates used with modems means that data is transmitted at a modest rate, and it is not usually difficult for the receiving equipment to keep up with a constant flow of data. Consider the popular rate of 300 baud. With ten bits per byte (including stop and start bits) this only gives a maximum transfer rate of 30 bytes per second. Except with very slow computers, terminal software written in BASIC is usually sufficient and it is not normally necessary to resort to machine code.

There is a slight complication to the RS232C system in that there are two types of RS232C equipment. There is data terminal equipment (DTE), and also data communications equipment (DCE). Data terminal equipment can be thought of as the main

8

piece of equipment, and it therefore receives on the data input terminal, and transmits on the data output connection. Data communications equipment does the opposite of this, and rather confusingly transmits on the input terminal and receives on the output. The reason for using this system is that it enables a lead having two 25 way D connectors to connect the two pieces of equipment together without the need for any crossed connections. This does of course work well if the two pieces of equipment you wish to connect together consist of one DTE and one DCE. If you have two pieces of equipment that are the same the use of a cross connected lead becomes necessary.

Some computers overcome this problem by having two serial ports, one configured as a DTE and the other having the DCE configuration. Therefore, provided the peripheral device and the computer both have the standard 25 way D connector there should be no difficulty in connecting the two pieces of equipment together using a standard RS232C connecting lead. The RS232C specification includes current limiting on the outputs, and connecting equipment to the wrong type of RS232C port should not cause any damage. A point worth bearing in mind is that any RS232C port can be connected to any other RS232C port, regardless of the equipment catagory, provided the right connections are provided, including cross coupling where necessary. The only difference between DTE and DCE equipment is the method of connection to the input/output socket. In my experience, except where a piece of equipment has twin RS232C port, with one DTE type and the other DCE configured, data inputs have always been inputs, and data outputs have always been outputs. If you have a computer with twin (DTE/DCE configured) ports the manual should make it clear which is which.

Modem Operation
For a serial data system to operate properly it is important that there is no serious distortion of the waveform, but the frequency response limitations of the telephone system would in fact produce quite severe distortion. Also, the inevitable noise in the form of "crackles" and "crashes" would give problems with corruption of data. These problems can be overcome by using a modem to transmit the serial data as two audio tones instead of

two voltage levels. The receiving modem demodulates the tones to convert them back into voltage levels which can drive an ordinary serial input. When using a modem, if you listen to the sounds coming from the telephone handset you should be able to hear stable tones when no data is being transmitted or received, and the warbling sound as the signal rapidly switches from one tone to the other when data is being transmitted.

There are two basic types of modem; the acoustically coupled and direct coupled types. The acoustically coupled type is the easiest to use as no connections to the telephone wires are needed. The telephone handset is placed into an acoustic coupler which takes signals from the modem and converts them into soundwaves which are fed down the system in the normal way. The coupler also includes a microphone which takes the sounds from the earpiece and converts them into electrical signals that are fed to the modem. The direct coupled type of modem must be connected direct to the telephone system. This has the advantage of reducing the number of processes to which the signals are subjected, and everything else being equal a direct coupled type should give better reliability than an acoustically coupled type. It has the disadvantage of needing a certain amount of wiring-in before it can be used, although this might not be necessary if your premises have telephone sockets fitted. With a double socket installed or a two-way adaptor fitted to a single type, and provided the appropriate plugs are fitted to the modem and telephone leads, both pieces of equipment can simply be plugged straight into the telephone system. The direct coupled type of modem might not be of much use if you wish to use a modem when travelling, and the acoustic coupled type offers the most versatile method of coupling which will work with most telephone handsets. The diversity of modern handsets does mean that it will not necessarily work satisfactorily with every handset that is encountered though.

A point which should be borne in mind is that in order to use a modem legally in Britain it must be a type approved by British Telecom, and it must be correctly installed. Approved equipment is clearly marked as such with the green circle of approval, while non-approved equipment should be marked with the red triangle "PROHIBITED" symbol. It is perhaps worth mentioning that the only difference between acoustically and direct coupled modems is the method of coupling to the telephone system, and they are fundamentally the same.

There are a number of modem standards, although most are not used in Britain. All the systems use the same basic tone encoding/decoding technique, but there are differences in the transmit/receive baud rates and audio tones used. The best type of modem to have depends on the intended application. If you just wish to swop programs with friends over the telephone system then practically any approved modem will suffice, provided you all have the same type or compatible types. If you wish to use one of the large telephone accessed databases and similar facilities then the company running the system will be able to advise on suitable equipment, and may even be able to supply suitable terminal units or adaptors for your computer. When using commercial facilities of this type there is normally a subscription fee and (or) other charges for using the service. Modems generally have to be of the 75/1200 baud variety, although some databases now seem to have facilities for both 75/1200 baud and 300/300 baud types.

Many computer hobbyists use modems for accessing non-commercial or semi-commercial systems. Amongst other things, these often offer a bulletin-board facility where messages for other users can be left. For example, if you are experiencing a problem with your computer it is possible that someone else has experienced and cured the same problem. If a message describing the problem is left on the bulletin-board it is possible that someone will see it and be able to leave a helpful reply. Systems of this type are generally set-up and run by computer enthusiasts, or are an off-shoot of a commercial system, and there is not normally a charge for using them, although parts of the system may be restricted to subscribers. Some of these systems carry information for users of a particular make of computer, and if you can find one that deals with the machine you own it could obviously be very useful indeed. There are a few shops (usually ones which sell electronic components and goods) which enable credit card orders to be placed via a modem, and information such as stock availability might also be available in some cases. For this type of thing A CCITT standard 300/300 baud modem is required. At present this type of thing is not very widespread, but it seems likely to gain in popularity in the future.

11

Multi-standard modems are available and if your intended applications are likely to require different standards then one of these is probably the best solution to the problem. However, bear in mind that standards which require different transmit and receive baud rates might be compatible with the modem, but might be beyond the capabilities of your computer's RS232C interface.

A term which confuses many people is "originate only", which suggests that the modem is only capable of transmitting, and can not receive signals. In fact this is not the case at all, and an "originate only" modem is capable of two way communication. In order to understand this term it is necessary to look in a little more detail at the way in which a modem functions. It was stated earlier that a modem converts the two input signal levels to two audio tones when transmitting, and that when decoding it translates these tones back into signal voltages again. This is almost true, but there are in fact four different tones used. The two transmission tones used by one modem are different to those used by the other one, so that when a modem transmits it does not pick-up and decode its own signal. This also permits full duplex operation in most cases.

Usually the transmitted signal is "echoed" back to the transmitting modem where it is demodulated and displayed on the monitor or television screen. This is useful as it will show up any corruption of the data that occurs through the system. Going back to the "originate only" term, this applies to a modem that can only transmit on one pair of frequencies, and receive on one pair of frequencies. This is satisfactory for many purposes, but it is not possible to communicate using two originate only modems as they will both transmit on the same pair of frequencies, and they will both receive on the same pair of frequencies (which will be different to the transmit frequencies). What is needed is one in the "originate" mode and one in the "answer" mode. Most modems now seem to offer both modes of operation.

One additional item that will be needed is some supporting software. In its most basic form this can be just a simple program consisting of about six lines of BASIC, but some relatively sophisticated and versatile communications programs are becoming available for an increasing number of computers.

Sophisticated programs do not actually do much more than very basic types, but are easier to set up for a given set of operating conditions and are generally much more convenient to use. Taking the most simple type of software, it does no more than transmit on the serial output anything that is typed into the computer, and print on the screen any data that is received at the serial input.

The simple program provided below is one that I have found to be useful when using a BBC model B computer with a 300/300 baud modem:-

```
5 REM BBC B TERMINAL PROGRAM
10 CLS
20 *FX7,3
30 *FX8,3
40 IF (?&FE08 AND 1)=1 THEN PRINT CHR$(?&FE09);
50 A$=INKEY$(0)
60 IF A$<>"" THEN ?&FE09=ASC(A$)
70 GOTO 40
```

This program may seem to be too simple to be of any practical value, but it is in fact perfectly adequate for many applications. As will be explained shortly, it does have limitations, and some applications would require software having a few more features. Line 10 simply clears the screen, and then lines 20 and 30 set the receive and transmit baud rates respectively. In this case both are set at 300 baud, but it is a useful (and unusual) feature of the BBC model B machine that it can operate with different receive and transmit baud rates. A check is made at line 40 to determine whether or not a character has been received by the serial port. To do this bit 0 of the serial interface device's control register is read, and this will be set to 1 if a character has been received but has not been read. Incidentally, the status register is at address &FE08, and the transmit/receive registers are at address &FE09. It is not always necessary to directly access the serial interface device in this way, and much the same effect can usually be obtained using the built-in software associated with the serial interface. This could in fact be achieved with the BBC model B machine using some of its *FX commands, but if you understand the computer's hardware it is often more simple to control it directly. It is also likely to give a higher operating speed, reducing the risk of the software being unable to keep up with a stream of received data. If a fresh character has been received line 40 prints it on the screen. Note the semicolon at the end of the PRINT instruction to ensure that the computer does not add any spaces between characters. The keyboard is read at line 50, and if a character has been typed into the keyboard, line 60 sends it to the serial port for transmission. Line 70 simply loops the program continuously, so that any received characters are almost immediately printed on the screen, and any characters typed onto the keyboard are almost instantly transmitted. It is quite easy to test software of this type, and it is merely necessary to couple the data output of the serial interface to the data input. Any characters typed into the computer should then appear on-screen (but this should not happen if the link on the serial port is removed).

Anyone who is reasonably good at writing sofware should not really have too much difficulty in producing a workable terminal program. The main limitation of a simple program of the type described previously is that it does not permit data to be stored for future use, and once it has been scrolled off the screen it is lost. Neither does it enable received data to be stored in memory as a program. These are features which it is certainly worthwhile incorporating into terminal programs. If you are not reasonably expert at writing programs it is not too important as there is no difficulty in buying suitable software for most computers. However, make sure that the software is compatible with both the modem you use as well as with the computer. It is quite common for terminal software to be supplied with modems, particularly types which are designed for use with a specific computer. In fact these are often sold as complete packages containing a modem, software, leads, and anything else that is needed to get the system up and running.

Modem Standards
I mentioned earlier that there is more than one modem standard, and that the main differences are in the modulation frequencies used and the intended baud rates. Here we will look at this topic in a little more detail, as well as taking a closer look at the way in which a modem functions.

There are two sets of modem standards, the American Bell ones and the European CCITT standards. At the time of writing this anyway, Bell standard modems can not be used legally in the U.K. as the frequencies used do not meet with British Telecom requirements. Multi-standard modems have to be modified to disable the Bell standard modes, or to modify them slightly, before they can be type approved. The Bell system is therefore largely of academic importance to British modem users, and would only be needed if American databases had to be accessed for some reason. The table that follows details the baud rates and modulation frequencies used in both the Bell and CCITT systems.

System	Baud	Duplex	Transmit		Receive	
			Space	Mark	Space	Mark
CCITT V21 Orig	300	Full	1180	980	1850	1650
CCITT V21 Ans	300	Full	1850	1650	1180	980
CCITT V23 Mode 1	600	Half	1700	1300	1700	1300
CCITT V23 Mode 2	1200	Half	2100	1300	2100	1300
CCITT V23 Back	75	·	450	390	450	390
Bell 103 Orig	300	Full	1070	1270	2025	2225
Bell 103 Ans	300	Full	2025	2225	1070	1270
Bell 202	1200	Half	2200	1200	2200	1200

The two Bell systems are obviously similar to the two CCITT systems, but in practice they are not sufficiently similar to give compatibility. As the Bell systems are not generally applicable in the U.K, we will not consider them further here.

The V21 system is probably the best for general purpose use as it enables a reasonably fast transfer of data in either direction. Also, as it offers full duplex operation the receiving equipment can "echo" received data back to the transmitting equipment, and an effective system of error checking can be implemented. On the other hand, the V23 system offers a significantly higher baud rate, but with only half duplex operation. It is important to realise that half duplex operation does not mean that communication in only one direction is possible (this is known as "simplex" operation). It means that the system can only provide a link in one direction at a time, and with suitable protocols implemented it is possible for two way communication to be provided. An effective protocol is

15

essential though, if a situation where both systems transmit at once is to be avoided. It is rather like a radio telephone system where communication is also only in one direction at a time, and the word "over" is used at the end of each message to indicate to the person at the other end of the system that it is their turn to speak. With a computer based system everything can be handled automatically though, and the user may not even be aware that the system is only functioning in one direction at a time.

The V23 system supports the 1200/75 baud system which was mentioned previously. This may seem to be a rather odd arrangement at first, but it is primarily intended for use with large databases. With these there is generally a large amount of data sent to the user from the database, and the higher baud rate is used for this. The lower baud rate is used for the user to send instructions to the database, and these are normally just very short instructions which can consequently be sent quite rapidly at a baud rate of only 75. In fact it is likely to be the users typing speed rather than the baud rate which dictates the rate at which characters are sent. 75 baud represents a maximum of 7.5 characters per second, or 450 characters per minute. In terms of words per minute this equates to something in the region of 75 to 90, which can only be achieved by very accomplished typists.

Figure 3 shows the basic arrangement used in a V21 modem. A modem is actually quite simple in the way it functions, but it is only fair to point out that practical units are actually quite complex, and until quite recently have been extremely expensive (over a thousand pounds each in fact). Although modern modems may not seem to be particularly cheap by comparison with some of the home computers they are designed to operate with, they do really represent excellent value for money.

If we now consider Figure 3 and start with the transmission side, the serial input signal is coupled to a tone generator circuit. This is usually a VCO (voltage controlled oscillator), which switches frequency in response to the changing input voltage, thus directly generating the two required tones. In a practical unit there would be some circuitry ahead of the tone generator to ensure that suitable control voltages are presented to the tone generator. If this was not done the tones would be dependent on the exact input voltages from the serial port, which could vary over a fairly wide

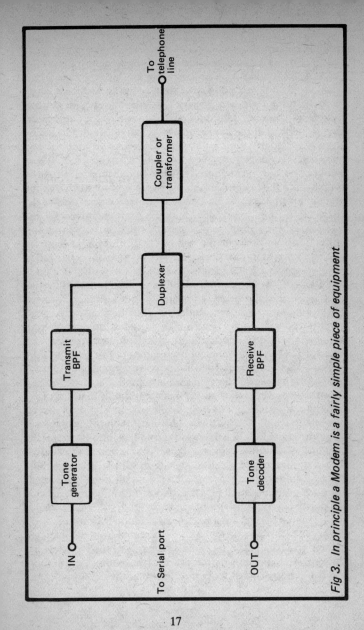

Fig 3. In principle a Modem is a fairly simple piece of equipment

17

range. Good accuracy of the tones is essential if the modem is to function properly in conjunction with other modem systems.

The second stage is a bandpass filter. This is a type which enables only a restricted band of frequencies to pass, and which severely attenuates any signals at frequencies outside this passband. There are two main reasons for including this filter. One is simply that the tone generator is unlikely to produce pure sinewave signals, and is almost certain to contain strong harmonics (multiples of the fundamental frequency). These would lie outside the permitted range of frequencies which can be coupled into the telephone system. The second reason is that the modulation process also tends to generate frequencies outside the permissible frequency range, and these are removed by the filtering. The range of pass frequencies depends on the transmitter tones in use, but the bandwidth is little more than the minimum necessary to accomodate the two tones. It does need to have a somewhat wider bandwidth than the theoretical minimum requirement as in practice significant delays are otherwise introduced, giving rise to "smearing" and a seriously distorted waveform at the receiving equipment. The filter is usually a good quality type which gives quite a high degree of attenuation even marginally outside the passband. A typical frequency response for tones of 1180 and 980Hz would be as shown in Figure 4.

The duplexer is a circuit which enables one signal to be sent out onto a pair of transmission lines while another signal is extracted from the lines. If the transmitted signal was simply to be fed direct onto the transmission lines it would effectively short circuit incoming signals and virtually eliminate them. The duplexer therefore provides a relatively loose coupling onto the transmission lines so that the incoming signal is not seriously attenuated. The transmitted and received signals should be at comparable levels. The duplexer is not needed if acoustic coupling is used, since the telephone itself plus the coupler then effectively provide the duplexing. If acoustic coupling is not used, the connections to the telephone system are made via an isolation transformer.

On the receiving side the signal is extracted from the duplexer and fed to a bandpass filter. This is primarily needed to attenuate the signal from the transmitter section of the modem, leaving only the two different tones from the modem at the other end of the

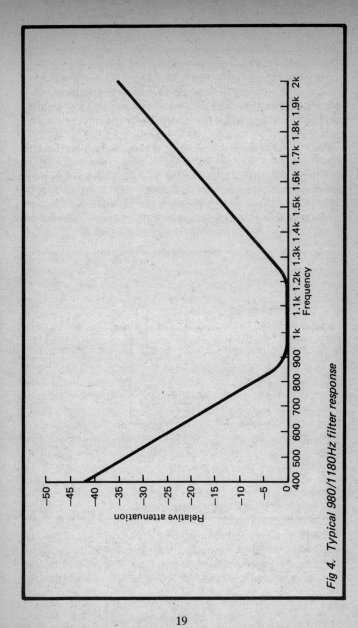

Fig 4. Typical 980/1180Hz filter response

system. It also helps to avoid problems with any noise on the telephone lines causing data to be corrupted. It is only fair to point out that with a very noisy line it is still possible for problems to occur, but considering the substantial amount of noise frequently encountered on the telephone system it is surprising how rarely glitches do occur provided the modem has been properly installed and set up.

The tone decoder has to convert the incoming tones back to signal voltages. Normally some signal conditioning circuits are used to provide an RS232C compatible output, instead of trying to design a circuit that will generate them directly. There are several types of tone decoder circuit which could be used, but the most common system is the PLL (phase locked loop) type. This uses the arrangement shown in the block diagram of Figure 5.

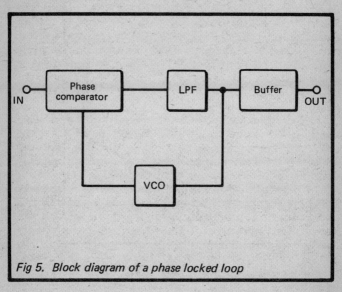

Fig 5. Block diagram of a phase locked loop

The input signal and the output of a VCO are fed to the two inputs of a phase comparator, and the output of the phase comparator is processed by a lowpass filter. The output from the phase comparator is a series of pulses, but when smoothed by the lowpass filter a DC voltage is obtained. The amplitude of this DC voltage depends on the relative phase and frequency of the two input signals. IF the VCO's output is at the lower frequency or slightly lagging in phase behind the input signal, the voltage goes to a relatively high figure. If the VCO is operating at a higher frequency than the input signal, or is slightly ahead in phase, the DC voltage goes to a low level.

The output from the lowpass filter is used as the control voltage for the VCO, and a simple feedback process results in the VCO being locked onto the same frequency as the input signal. If the VCO was to drift higher than the input frequency for some reason, the control voltage would be reduced, counteracting the drift and locking the VCO back onto the same frequency. Of more importance, if the input frequency changes then the same feedback system operates, and the VCO tracks the frequency of the input signal. It is not the signal from the oscillator that we require here, but it is the output voltage from the lowpass filter that is required. This varies in sympathy with the input frequency and therefore constitutes the decoded output. This signal is extracted via a buffer amplifier which ensures that loading on the output does not upset the correct operation of the phase locked loop.

This may seem like a rather over-complicated way of doing things, and there are actually more simple approaches to the problem. However, phase locked loops give excellent results and are much used in communications systems. They were originally developed for space communications incidentally.

If we return to Figure 3, a practical modem is generally somewhat more complex than this would suggest as there are some common features which are not included in this diagram. The most obvious one in two sets of filters plus some switching to enable both answer and originate modes to be provided. The switching often includes a "test" setting where the modem transmits and receives on the same pair of frequencies. This is useful when testing the system as it enables the modem to transmit to itself, and any characters that are transmitted are effectively echoed back to the receiver and should be displayed on the monitor or television screen. The tone decoder circuit often includes a lock indicator circuit, which simply switches on an indicator light on the front panel when the modem has locked onto an input signal. Another requirement for a modem is some form of power source. Some are battery powered, and an acoustically coupled battery powered type, if used in conjunction with a portable computer, is obviously ideal for use when travelling around. However, most types have a built-in power supply for mains use and are not portable. A few types which are specifically designed for use with one computer are powered from the computer.

Extra Features

So far we have only considered basic modems, but as new modems come onto the market they seem to be equipped with an ever increasing range of advanced features. Some of these are extremely useful, but none could really be regarded as essential. Most of the more common ones are listed below, together with a brief explanation of each one.

Software Control

This is where the modem can be controlled by the computer as well as by using conventional controls on the front panel. This is not really necessary for normal use, but some of the special features described below are only possible with the aid of software control. Software control is perhaps not a very apt term, as although it enables the terminal program to control certain aspects of the modem, it usually requires an extra cable to provide connections from the modem to (as an example) the user port of the computer. It therefore involves the use of extra hardware and is not implemented solely in software. A software approach using control codes via the serial interface to control the modem might be practical, but I have not yet encountered such a system.

Auto Dial

As this term implies, it provides automatic dialing, normally by the computer under software control. This is a very convenient way of doing things, and gives greater flexibility than might at first appear to be the case. With most systems a directory of numbers can be held on disc or cassette, and the required number is selected and then automatically dialed. Other features are possible, such as automatic redialing of engaged numbers and dialing of several numbers until a vacant line is obtained. This type of facility is more useful than you might think, as a great deal of time can be taken up repeatedly dialing the number of a database (or whatever) until an answer is obtained. Things may improve as time passes, but at the time of writing this, it seems to take half a dozen or more attempts before most systems can be accessed (somewhat less if you are prepared to wait until very late at night).

Auto Answer

This is another term which is largely self explanatory, and it is where a modem will start to operate automatically when a call is received. It operates in a manner similar to a telephone answering machine, and could in fact be used as such with suitable software, but only for callers who have a modem of course. If you wish to set up your own bulletin board or something of this type it is virtually essential to have an auto answer modem plus software that will enable users to automatically access the information they require or feed it into the system. The alternative of manning the system for the entire time it is on-line is not likely to be a practical proposition.

Reverse Prestel

Prestel is a database service run by British Telecom, and it originally used only a 1200/75 baud (CCITT V23) system. Modems designed for accessing Prestel and similar systems are of little use for anything else. For instance, it is not possible for two users to communicate with one another using modems of this type, since they will both transmit on the same pair of frequencies and receive on the same pair of frequencies. This would be like trying to communicate using two V21 standard modems with both set to the answer mode or both set to the originate mode. Trying to communicate with two V23 modems gives the arrangement shown in Figure 6(a), whereas what is needed is an arrangement of the type outlined in Figure 6(b). This second set-up can be achieved if one of the modems can be set to the so called "reverse Prestel" mode, which gives transmission at 1200 baud and reception at 75 baud. Some modems implement a 1200/1200 baud system for user-to-user communications. Note though, that the

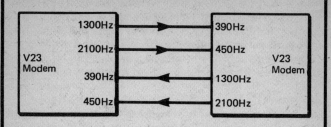

(a)

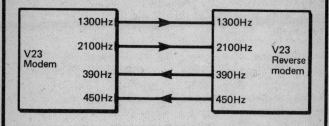

(b)

Fig 6. (a) Two V23 (1200/75) modems can not communicate with one another. One of the modems must be set to the "Reverse" mode, as in (b)

24

1200/1200 mode is a half duplex one, whereas 1200/75–75/1200 systems give full duplex operation (albeit with a very limited operating speed in one direction). The 1200/1200 baud system is better if a lot a data has to be passed through the system in both directions, but somewhat more sophisticated software is needed in order to implement user-transparent two way communications.

Auto Speed Selection
Another fairly self explanatory term. Here the modem automatically sets itself to the correct operating standard when it receives a signal from another modem. The different frequencies used in the various standards enable this facility to operate. Some databases will work with both V21 and V23 modems, and these either have separate numbers for the two systems, or an automatic speed selection system so that one telephone number can be used for both types of modem.

World Standard
This term can be a bit misleading in that it suggests a modem which uses a standard that is used throughout the world. The alternative term of "multistandard" is perhaps a better one, since modems of this type are ones which can handle any Bell or CCITT modem standard. A true world standard or multistandard type should include the modified Bell standard mode to permit legal operation in this mode in the U.K. "Dual" or "twin" standard modems are types which support both the V21 and V23 CCITT modes (which are all that most users in the U.K. require).

PSS
While explaining technical terms it is perhaps worth briefly mentioning the term "PSS", or "Packet Switched System", which you might occasionally encounter. Put in a very over-simplified manner, this is a system which enables several sources and destinations to use one long distance link (often via satelite). This is done by splitting up messages into blocks of data of a certain size, or "packets" as they are termed, with each packet containing an address code which enables the intended receiving terminal to sort it out from the mass of unwanted data it receives. In fact with some systems the packets also contain a sequence number so

25

that messages can be reassembled in the correct order at the receiving terminal if they are sent out of order. The purpose of all this is to make more efficient use of expensive long distance data links, and it is something that is, at present anyway, mainly of interest to commercial users.

In Practice

So far we have considered a lot of background information, and now to complete this chapter we will take a look at how a modem can be used in practice. The first step is to select a modem, and this is a matter of first finding out just what can be obtained for your particular computer. With a computer such as the BBC model B which has a versatile serial port there is a relatively large range available, but for some machines there is a very limited choice indeed. If you have a computer for which there is only a restricted range available it might be that a special modem interface of some kind or an add-on RS232C port is available, and that this will open up a wider choice. If you are unlucky it might be that there is no suitable modem available for your computer, and that no serial or modem interface is available either. Most machines are catered for but if a search of advertisements in computer magazines and enqiries at local computer shops fail to bring results, the only option (apart from giving up) is to obtain the cheapest computer for which you can obtain a modem. This may seem to be a little extravagant, but a cheap computer (especially if you can find a suitable secondhand machine) plus a modem need not cost a great deal, and can provide the user with a lot of fun and interest.

If you are unsure what type of modem will best suit your needs, probably the best course of action is to choose the least expensive type that will operate with both the V21 and V23 standards. This should not cost an excessive amount, but will give sufficient versatility to leave little risk of you rapidly outgrowing the modem and needing a more expensive and sophisticated type. A modem with a lot of clever features can be more convenient in use than a type having only a very basic specification, but do not loose sight of the fact that an expensive modem still only provides the same basic function as an equivalent without the "frills".

It is important to bear in mind that the modem and the computer are quite useless without some supporting software.

Unless you are confident that you can write your own terminal program it would be advisable not to buy a modem unless you are certain that suitable software can also be obtained. If software is supplied with the modem bear in mind that this must be designed for your particular make and model of computer if it is to be of any use.

Similarly, a connecting lead will be needed in order to connect the modem to the computer, and the system is totally useless without this lead. A suitable lead might be supplied with the modem, or might be available as an extra. If you are handy with a soldering iron you might be able to make up a suitable lead, and as explained previously, only three connecting wires are needed (the two signal leads plus earth). If you can obtain a complete package consisting of the modem, terminal software for your computer, and any necessary connecting leads, then this is probably the best way of doing things. Apart from being a very convenient solution, it could well prove to be the least expensive in the long run.

Provided your premises are fitted with a standard 4 way telephone socket there should be no difficulty in connecting everything up. If the modem has a telephone socket fitted the method of connection shown in Figure 7 is used. If it does not, a two way adaptor must be fitted to the normal telephone socket so that the method of connection shown in Figure 8 can be adopted. The connectors we are concerned with here are of course the new four way type, and not the old 4 way jack type. The old type are visually very much like the jack plugs used with headphones and earphones, whereas the new type are rectangular rather than round. Confusingly, the new type are sometimes sold as telephone "jacks", but as long as you see what you are buying there should be no risk of confusing the two and purchasing the wrong thing.

It has been assumed above that the modem you use is a direct coupled type, and if you opt for an acoustically coupled type there is obviously no connections to the telephone system to be made. The modem will instead have a so called "reverse telephone", into which a standard telephone handset is pushed, making sure it is fitted the right way round. The couplers are designed to accept a reasonable range of telephone handsets, but anything even slightly exotic, such handsets which have a built-in keypad or

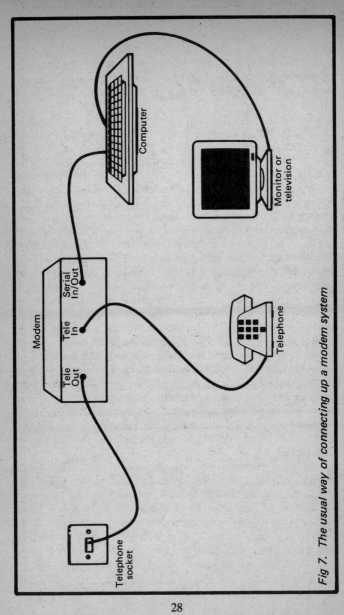

Fig 7. The usual way of connecting up a modem system

28

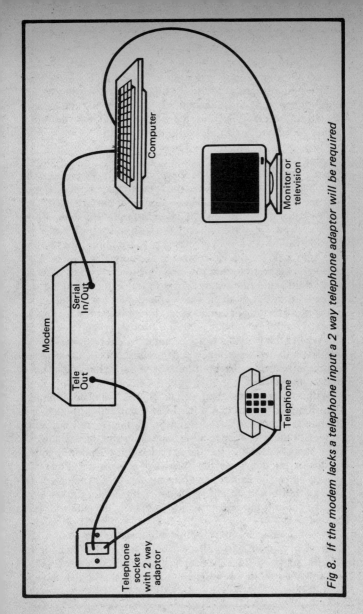

Fig 8. If the modem lacks a telephone input a 2 way telephone adaptor will be required

dial, are likely to give poor results or to prove to be totally unusable with the modem. Couplers are designed to exclude as much background noise and vibration as possible, but by their nature it is not possible to obtain complete isolation from physical noise. When using a modem of this type it is important that there should not be a high ambient sound level, and that the modem is positioned where it will not be disturbed.

Making Contact
Having reached the stage where everything is connected up, the terminal software is loaded into the computer and is running, and you are ready to go, the obvious question is "what now"? This really depends on just how you intend to use the system. If you have a friend with a modem and you wish to swop programs via the telephone system, or something of this nature, then the first step is to make telephone contact in the normal way. You must decide on the word format you are going to use, as well as things such as the baud rate, who is going to transmit data and who is going to receive it, or in the case of full duplex operation, who is going to use the originate mode and who is going to use the answer mode. Usually full duplex (300/300) baud operation is used for this type of thing, with a word format of 8 data bits, one stop bit and no parity. However, the word format and mode used are not important, except in that both ends of the system must be set up to match one another.

With contact established the modem is switched "on-line" (which merely means that it has been connected through to the telephone socket and is ready for use), it is then merely necessary to replace the telephone handset and commence the exchange of data. It is not actually essential to replace the telephone handset on its rest, but doing so avoids the risk of noise or vibration being picked-up by the handset and causing data to be corrupted. Of course, with an acoustically coupled modem there is no "on-line" switch, and it is put on-line simply by placing the handset in the coupler.

When accessing a database, bulletin board, or a system of this general type, again start with the modem switched off-line (or the handset removed from the coupler), and dial the number of the system you wish to access. There is a strong chance that the line

30

will be engaged, and it can take a large number of attempts to get into some of the more popular systems at times of peak popularity. If there are several systems that are of interest to you it is a good idea to go through the list of numbers in rotation until you are successful. The usual ringing tones will then be heard, and then after a few seconds have elapsed a high pitched tone should be heard. This is produced by the modem answering your call, and indicates that it is time to switch your modem to the "on-line" setting, and replace the handset. Note that you must switch the modem on-line before replacing the handset in its rest. Switching the modem on-line will "hold" the line until the end of the session when you log-off by switching back to the off-line setting. If you replace the handset before switching the modem on-line this will terminate the call and you will have to redial the number. Always remember to switch the modem off-line at the end of each session. Not doing so is rather like not replacing the handset in its rest at the end of a call, and it could result in a line being blocked unnecessarily, and could conceivably result in a very large telephone bill.

Of course, before trying to access a system you must discover the baud rate(s) used, and the word format required, so that your equipment can be set up accordingly. There may be a switch with options such as "test", "full duplex", and "half duplex", and this should be set to the "full duplex" position. With a modem that has both answer and originate modes it is the originate mode that is required (as you are originating the call). With "Prestel" and "Reverse Prestel" modes it is obviously the "Prestel" mode that is required.

Assuming that everything is set up correctly, when the modem at the database receives the tone from your modem it will respond by sending a page of data which should fill the screen over a period of a few seconds. Normally this page gives the name of this system, plus possibly some technical details about it, followed by a menu giving a list of options. With a complex system the first page may in fact just give some background information, and there will then be a message at the bottom of the screen which will say something like "Press Any Key To Continue". There may be several pages to go through, but eventually most systems provide a menu. With the large databases it is normally only possible to fully access them if you are a subscriber, and you have been assigned an identity number. This number has to be given, followed by some form of password or code. Unless the correct pass code for the identity number is given, access to the system is blocked. Without something of this kind it would be possible for anyone to access the system by simply giving any valid identity number. A suitable number could soon be found with a little trial and error. "Hackers" is the name used for people who make a hobby out of getting into restricted areas of systems, but in some circumstances this can be illegal, and it is not a topic which will be persued in this book.

Even if full access to a system is not available to you, some sort of demonstration facility might be. With Prestel a customer identity number of 4444444444 ("4" ten times) takes you into a set of demonstration pages. Use 4444 as the personal identity number. The idea of these is to give you an idea of what the system has to offer, with a view to persuading you to take out a sub-scription. If you are considering joining a system of this type it is well worthwhile going through the demonstation pages, and they should help to give you an idea of just what the system can and can not do.

Small systems are usually free for anyone to access, and early in the proceedings you will be presented with a menu with various options. If we take as an example the Maptel system which I often use, this is run by Maplin Electronic Supplies Ltd., a company which specialises in the sale of electronic components, computer accessories, and similar goods. Maptel (the telephone number for which is Southend-On-Sea (0702) 552941) can be used to obtain such things as information on their new product lines, price and stock level information, and news of the club for Atari users which is run by some members of staff. It is also possible to place an order provided you have a customer number and a suitable credit card. These facilities are fairly typical, although most systems do not provide all of them. Many systems are run by private indi-viduals or educational establishments, and they provide infor-mation on a particular type or make of computer, often including a facility for users to communicate with each other so that they can swop ideas, help each other to solve problems, and so on. The ability to order goods via a modem system is relatively rare at present, and is mainly restricted to companies selling electronic goods of one kind or another, but this is an area which could well expand considerably in the future.

Most systems are easy to use, with the extensive use of menus and prompts which tell you exactly what to do in order to obtain the required option. If we take Maptel as an example, and assume that stock availability information is required on some goods, the appropriate menu option for that key plus a carriage return are entered (most systems require a carriage return after each piece of data has been entered). This gives the following message:-

CAN ENTER A STOCK CODE, END, OR ANY
VALID MAPTEL COMMAND (TYPE HELP)

By finding the order codes for the items that are of interest in the Maplin catalogue, and then typing these into the computer, Maptel provides a brief description of each item (so that it should be obvious if you have made a mistake with the code), together with the current price of each item and the number in stock at that moment. By typing in the appropriate command you can move on to another facility of the system, or if you do not know the command required, "HELP" and a carriage return can be entered. A page which explains the system is then provided, and this should give you the necessary information on how to progress to the facility you require. If you get into difficulty with any system it is worthwhile trying "HELP", as this will often provide information that will get you out of difficulties and into the facility you require.

Although most systems are menu driven, and if there are a large number of pages available there will be a whole string of menus to gradually direct users to the page they require, it is often possible to jump direct to the page you want provided you know its number. Thus newcomers to the system can gradually home-in on the information they require, but experienced users can jump straight to the information they want without having to tediously go through menu option after menu option. There is normally a way of logging off from the system (typing "END" and return in the case of MAPTEL) but if you get completely stuck in the middle of a system, or a bad telephone line results in corruption of data to the point where effective communication with the system is lost, simply switching the modem off-line to end the call might be the only answer. This should not crash the system you were using though, and it should reset itself ready to operate properly again from the beginning when the next call is received.

One obvious problem is that of finding out just what systems are available, their telephone numbers, technical details, and what they have to offer. This is something that is constantly changing and a list of telephone numbers plus basic system details will not be provided here as it would almost certainly be hopelessly out of date by the time this book reached the shops. Many computer magazines give telephone numbers and fundamental details of the current range of on-line datbases, bulletin boards etc., and looking through some recent issues of computer magazines should tell you most of what you need to know. "Personal Computer World" is one that I have found to be very useful in this respect, but as modems become more popular a larger range of magazines are starting to give this type of information. In fact one or two magazines have their own systems which can be accessed to obtain the latest news in the computer world. Some modems and terminal software packages are supplied complete with some useful numbers and details, although this information might not be particularly up-to-date. You may find it necessary to access a number of systems in order to sort out those that are of real interest and use from a list of likely contenders, and it is well worthwhile exploring a good selection of systems.

This raises what may seem to be a obvious point to watch, but one which it is easy to overlook. Even where there is no cost for accessing and using a system, there is still the telephone bill to contend with. It is very easy to loose track of time when using a modem, and to incur large telephone bills as a result. Many users impose a strict limit on the time spent each day using their modem, and carefully monitor the on-line time. This might seem a rather miserly approach, but it ensures that the bill can be kept within a predictable and acceptable limits and avoids shocks when the telephone bill arrives. Of course, it is cheaper to use the phone at off-peak times (after 6pm and weekends), but, unfortunately, these times are the ones when most people are trying to access systems, and you may have difficulty logging-on to your selected system. Also, not all systems operate 24 hours a day, and some only offer a limited service outside normal hours. Therefore, the option of access during cheap-rate telephone hours may not be available. Bear in mind that accessing a local system (which means one within about 56 kilometres as far as the telephone system is concerned) is normally cheaper than accessing one which lies outside your local telephone area. Some of the large databases are organised in such a way that they can be accessed at local rates from practically anywhere in the country.

As (hopefully) this chapter has shown, a modem can greatly expand the usefulness of a computer outfit, and increase the enjoyment gained from it, but is not too difficult to set up and use successfully. As with most technical hobbies, it is very easy to be put off by the jargon and complexities, but with a little effort the problems encountered can be overcome without too much difficulty.

Chapter 2

LOCAL NETWORKS

Modems and tone encoding/decoding systems are only required where data links over fairly large distances are required. Where computers just a few metres apart must be linked it is possible to directly connect RS232C or RS423 interfaces, or parallel interfaces if both computers are equipped with a suitable type. This makes it possible to link many computers into a sort of very basic local network using nothing more than a connecting lead and some simple software, as we shall see later in this chapter.

Local networks (also known as local area networks or "LAN"s) may seem to be of limited value, but in the right circumstances they can in fact be of tremendous value. Some networks are very complex affairs which enable a large number of computers to be connected together, and peripherals such as printers and disc drives to be shared between the computers. This can be very useful in business systems and in educational establishments, where such a set up is virtually as good as having a set of peripherals for each computer, but the cost is very much less. Such complex and expensive arrays of equipment are not really applicable to most home computer users though, and sophisticated networking systems are generally only worthwhile when applied to such a set-up. With a relatively simple system the additional cost of the network might well be greater than the cost of providing separate peripherals for each computer. Networking could still be a worthwhile proposition, but only if a sophisticated system to provide communications between the computers is required.

Few home computers, as yet anyway, seem to be equipped with some form of network interface, or have an optional network interface available. However, it is a feature that seems to be slowly gaining in popularity. The BBC computers have the optional ECONET interface, which is a sophisticated and relatively expensive type. The network which is probably most familiar to home computer users is the more basic but inexpensive Sinclair type (as fitted to the QL computer, and to the Interface 1 for the Spectrum computer). There are two basic connection methods for networking systems, the "chain" (or "daisy chain") system of Figure 9(a), and the "star" set-up of Figure 9(b). Normally with the star system one computer in the system acts as the controller, and all the others connect to it. The computers are not all equal, with the controller playing the dominant role.

With the chain system, which is the one adopted for the Sinclair network, each computer has a pair of sockets at the back (these are ordinary 3.5 millimetre jack sockets in the case of the Sinclair system). One socket of the first computer is wired through to a socket on the second machine, the spare, socket on the second computer is wired through to one of the sockets on the third computer, and so on. There is a limit to the number of computers that can be chained together, but this is normally quite high, and is up to sixty four in the case of the Sinclair networking system.

One popular misconception about this type of interface is that each computer has an input socket and an output socket. In fact the two sockets are wired together inside the computer, and it does not matter which one is connected to the previous computer in the network, and which one connects to the next computer in the chain. Both sockets have the ability to act as inputs or as outputs, and are what is called "bidirectional". As each pair of sockets is wired in parallel, obviously they must both act as inputs or both operate as outputs, and split operation is not possible (or necessary).

The general scheme of things is to have all the sockets normally set as inputs, or "listeners" as they are sometimes termed. If a computer is instructed to output data then its network sockets are switched to the output mode, and it sends the data to every other computer connected to the network. A device which sends data is sometimes called a "talker" in this context. With a system of this type the manual usually warns against connecting the system into a loop (i.e. connecting the spare socket on the first computer in the chain to the unused socket on the final computer in the network). There is no obvious reason why this should not be done since these two sockets are connected together anyway via the chain of connecting wires, but it would obviously be superfluous to add a lead to connect them together. Possibly problems with an earth loop could arise, but if the manual for the network warns

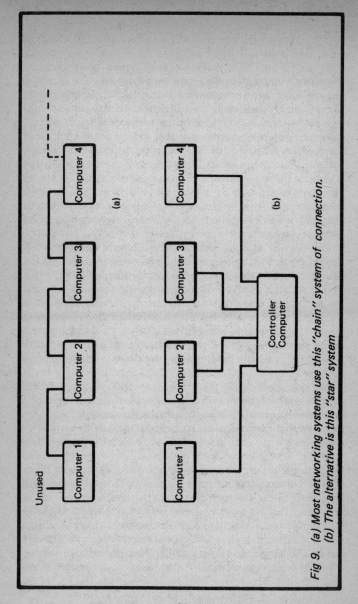

Fig 9. (a) Most networking systems use this "chain" system of connection.
(b) The alternative is this "star" system

against using the loop connection, then the sensible course of action is to make sure it is absent.

Although data is fed to every listener in the network, with a practical system it is normally possible for data to be directed to just one device. This is done using a simple system of addressing, where transmitted data is preceded by a header code which includes the address of the computer to which the data is being directed. The user must assign the address number to each computer in the network. With the Sinclair system the default address is 1, and with only two computers in the network they can both have the same address, making it unnecessary to assign an address to either machine. It is alright for both machines to have the same address simply because the bidirectional system ensures that a computer can not pick up the data it is sending, and the problems this could cause are avoided.

With most networks, including the Sinclair one, the system is a little more sophisticated than the one outlined above in that the header information includes the address of the computer sending the data as well as the address of the intended recipient computer. In order to exchange data the talker must transmit using the correct destination address, and the listener must be set to respond to the correct source address. This would limit the system to communication between only two computers at once, which is not always what is required. For example, a typical network application is to load a program from the single disc drive in the system into one of the computers, and to then transmit the program from this computer to all the other computers on the network. This would be a rather tedious process if it had to be accomplished by sending the program to the computers one by one.

The usual solution to the problem, and the one implemented in the Sinclair network, is to have a "broadcast" address (which is address 0 in the Sinclair system). With the program transmitted to this address, all the other computers in the system will receive the program provided they are set to receive data from address 0. The ability of computers not to receive data sent out on the broadcast address unless directed to do so is an important one, since it will not always be necessary to send data from one computer to all the others. On some occasions it might be necessary to (say) send one program to half of the computers, and another program to the other half. By broadcasting first one program then the other, and programming the recipient computers correctly, this is easily achieved.

The Sinclair network includes a sort of pseudo handshake arrangement where data is not sent unless or until the recipient computer is ready to do so. This is not practical using the broadcast address though, and any data sent to this address is sent at once whether any computer on the network is ready to receive it or not.

A network of the type used in the Sinclair computers could in fact be wired in a sort of star arrangement, but with the controller simply acting as a point where all the network sockets could be wired together, rather than acting as a true controller. For a simple network the chain arrangement is far more practical though, since every computer in the system is identical and there is no no need for a special controller type. Also, the chain system is generally much easier to wire up in practice. Therefore, any fairly simple form of network you encounter is almost certain to use the chain method of connection.

Home-Spun Networks
For most home computer users a full blown network is not needed, and neither is a relatively simple networking system come to that. In most cases all that is required is the ability to simply couple one computer to another so that data can be exchanged in either direction. A typical application would be in some form of game where both players have their own computer and display. The game could be anything from a board game such as chess to a highly complex arcade style game. A game such as "battleships" lends itself well to this type of thing.

Whatever the intended application, many computers provide some means of communicating with other computers, although in some cases communications is restricted to a link between two computers of the same type, or perhaps to links between two computers from the same manufacturer.

One popular misconception is that two computers can be linked via their cassette interfaces, using a method of connection along the lines shown in Figure 10. The first problem with doing this

40

is that practically every computer has its own type of cassette interface which will not function when used in conjunction with a different computer. With computers such as those from Commodore and Atari the cassette interface is common to all the

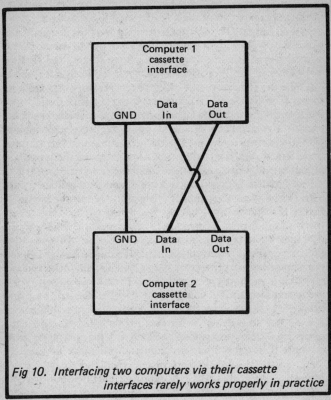

Fig 10. Interfacing two computers via their cassette interfaces rarely works properly in practice

home computers from the particular manufacturer concerned. This is still rather restrictive in that the cassette port of (say) an Atari 600XL is the same as that fitted to the Atari 800XL, but it is still totally different to the cassette ports on Commodore and Sinclair machines, and every other computers manufactured by someone other than Atari.

This lack of compatibility between computers from different manufacturers is something that it often of little consequence, since in many cases it is two computers of the same type that one wishes to link. However, it still leaves a couple of problems. The main one is that most cassette interfaces are designed to feed into the microphone input of the recorder, and to be driven from the earphone output. The microphone input requires a signal level which is typically only about one thousanth to one ten thousanth as strong as the output from the earphone socket. The cassette interface accordingly provides an output level which is very much less than the signal level it expects to receive from the earphone socket. The discrepancy is not normally anything like the factor of one to ten thousand times mentioned above, as cassette interfaces provide a relatively strong output signal to ensure compatibility with insensitive recorders. The discrepancy is almost invariably there though, and is more than adequate to ensure that a cassette output can not drive a cassette input of the same type properly.

The problem is not insurmountable, and an amplifier should cure the problem. For anyone wishing to try this the circuit of Figure 11 might be suitable. However, I have not been able to test this with a wide range of computers, and can consequently give no guarantees that it will be satisfactory in every case. Anyone with a little experience of electronic construction should be able to build the amplifier at very low cost though, and it might form the basis for some interesting experimentation. Even if two cassette ports are linked successfully, unless you understand the hardware and firmware of the computers in some detail, it could be difficult to get the link to provide useful data exchanges. The BASIC or operating system commands associated with the port might allow no more than transmitting or loading of programs. Fortunately there is a trend with the more recent computers to allow more sophisticated use of the cassette interface, and this is also possible with some older designs. This usually takes the form of "channels", where a channel can be opened to the cassette port so that it can be read or sent data without any difficulty.

Serial Links
If the two computers that are to be linked have an RS232C or RS423 serial interface, or an add-on interface of this type can

be obtained, then this probably represents the best method of linking them. Incidentally, RS232C and RS423 ports are fully

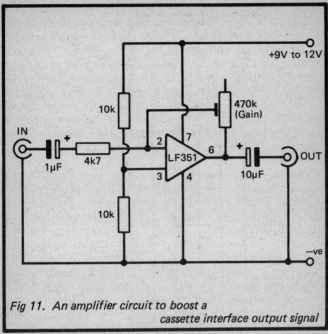

*Fig 11. An amplifier circuit to boost a
cassette interface output signal*

compatible with one another, and there should be no difficulty in linking an RS232C port to and RS423 type. Apart, that is, from the problems that could arise when linking two RS232C ports or two RS423 ports. We will consider the possible pitfalls in detail a little later. Connecting two serial ports together is not difficult, and the basic set-up required is shown in Figure 12. In its most simple form the link requires just three wires: an earth connection, plus separate leads to carry the data in each direction. The "data input" and "data output" terminals are cross coupled so that the output from one computer is fed to the input of the other. This is rather like a full duplex modem link, but as only short distances (up to about 15 metres) are involved there is no need for

43

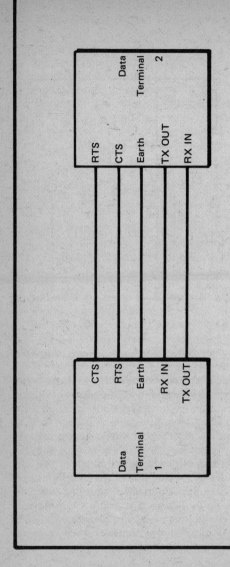

Fig 12. Connecting two data terminals for full duplex operation

44

the modems. As this three-wire method of connection does not include handshake lines to regulate the flow of data it is essential that the baud rate is a fairly low one that restricts the rate at which data is transferred to one which both computers can handle. Otherwise a severe loss of data would result, making the system unusable. The maximum rate which is acceptable depends on the computer concerned, and the way in which it is being used, but 300 baud will be satisfactory in most cases, and a rate as high as 1200 baud might be satisfactory in some cases. The highest acceptable rate can be found by trial and error if necessary, or in an application where only small amounts of data will be exchanged a fairly low baud rate will probably be perfectly acceptable.

If machine code or assembly language routines are being used to handle the data transfer it is likely that any baud rate up to the maximum standard rate of 19200 could be used. This represents a transfer rate of about 1920 bytes per second, which is well within the capabilities of assembly language or machine code.

The two additional lines must be connected if handshaking is to be implemented. If the receiving device is unable to keep up with the rate at which data is being transmitted, it can then signal to the transmitting terminal to stop sending until it has processed the current data and it is ready to receive fresh data again. The handshake line is taken positive if the receiving terminal is ready to receive data, or negative if a hold-off is required. Two handshake lines are required because separate lines are used to regulate the flow of data in each direction.

In an application of this type the use of handshaking is generally of little value. It enables high baud rates to be used, but with the handshake lines providing a hold-off for much of the time a high baud rate with handshaking does not provide a significantly faster transfer of data than the maximum baud rate that does not require handshaking. In fact it is not necessarily any faster at all. I always avoid using the handshake lines where this is possible. An important point to note is that some serial interfaces will not output any data unless the handshake input (Request To Send or "RTS") is held in the active state (i.e. taken about 12 volts positive). Some serial ports have a +12 volt output which can be used to tie the RTS line to a suitable potential, but if not, the only solution might be to connect up the handshake lines, even though they will not play an active role, but will simply provide a suitable static signal level to the RTS terminals.

A possible source of confusion with serial interfaces is the fact that there are two types of RS232C interface. These are the DTE (data terminal equipment) and and the DCE (data communications equipment) types. They differ only in that the data terminal equipment, as one would expect, sends data on its "data output" terminal and receives via its "data input" terminal. With data communications equipment data is sent on the "data input" terminal and received on the "data output" terminal. The handshake inputs and outputs are similarly transposed. This may seem pointless, but the original idea was to have a DCE device at one end of a link and a DTE type at the other. The two can then be connected by a standard RS232C cable having two 25 way D connectors with no cross coupling.

Figure 2 gives details of the standard method of connection for a standard RS232C port. However, it is only fair to point out that many computers and other pieces of equipment which have a serial port do not use this type of connector. This is understandable, since the vast majority of the twenty five available terminals are left unused in most pieces of equipment. The majority of the terminals have been assigned a function, but in practice only the five main lines (earth, input, output, and the two handshake lines) are normally implemented. The relatively large expense of a 25 way D connector is therefore not really justified, and cheaper types such as 5 way DIN connectors are often used instead. On the other hand, this is rather inconvenient in that in many cases it prevents a standard RS232C connecting lead from being used to connect two computers together. For some combinations of computer it might be possible to find a ready-made lead, but in most cases it will be a matter of buying some 3 or 5 way cable plus the appropriate types of plug, and then connecting it all up yourself.

Returning to the topic of DCE and DTE equipment, most computers and other items of equipment which have serial ports almost invariably have DTE types, and the terminal designated as the output in the connection diagram in the manual should therefore be the terminal that supplies transmitted data. Similarly, the terminal designated as the input should be an input, and the handshake lines should be as designated in the diagram. This means that if the two computers to be connected do both happen to have the standard 25 way D type connector, it is a cross-coupled rather than a "straight" connecting lead that will be required.

One exception where a DCE RS232C port might be encountered is if you have a computer with twin serial ports. It is then common practice for one port to be connected as a DCE type and the other to be connected as a DTE type. The computer's manual should make it quite clear which port is which if this should be the case. It is important to realise that the only difference between the two types of port is their method of connection to the D connector, and that any RS232C port can be coupled to any other RS232C port, regardless of whether each one is of the DTE variety or a DCE type. There is current limiting on RS232C outputs, and accidentally connecting two outputs together should not cause any damage to either interface.

Word Format
The right method of connection and matching baud rates is not sufficient to guarantee a proper data transfer between two serial ports, and the word format also has to be the same at both interfaces. With RS423 ports the standard word format is 8 data bits, 1 stop bit, and no parity. Consequently the problem of matched word formats does not arise when connecting two RS423 interfaces. When connecting an RS423 interface to an RS232C type it is obviously necessary to set the RS232C port for a word format of 8 data bits, 1 stop bit, and no parity, since the word format of the RS423 port will not be changeable. In fact it is sometimes possible to alter the word format of an RS423 port, but the computer's manual is unlikely to include details of how this can be done, and it will only be possible if you have in-depth knowledge of the computer.

There are a large number of possible word formats, and any format that can be provided by both computers is likely to be satisfactory in practice. A format with 8 data bits is generally preferable to a 7 data bit type, since 7 bit codes can not handle numbers in the range 128 to 255. These may not be required, and this really depends on the type of data transfer required, but the use of an 8 bit format avoids the possibility of problems occurring due to the loss of the most significant bit. When transfering data between computers of two different types bear in mind that their character sets will almost certainly contain some differences, and that in some cases not even the alpha-numeric characters will have the same codes.

If the two interfaces can not be set to have any matching word format (which is highly unlikely), it might still be worthwhile experimenting to see if some combination of word formats gives satisfactory operation. This is sometimes possible, and in particular, the wrong number of stop bits is often of no significance in practice.

Commodore Computers

The Commodore VIC-20 and Commodore 64 computers have a user port which can be used to provide an RS232C style link. Some later Commodore computers have a VIC-20/C64 style user port which might offer the same facility, but I have not had any experience with these and can not definitely confirm this. The serial interface of the VIC-20 and Commodore 64 computers is unusual in two respects. The first is that it only provides 0 and 5 volt output levels rather than the normal RS232C voltages of +12 volts and −12 volts. An adaptor is therefore needed in order to give proper RS232C operation with the correct signal voltages. However, there is no need for any processing of the signals in order to provide communications between one Commodore serial port and another. The output signals are only at 0 and 5 volts, but this is all that input terminals require, and the inputs and outputs are therefore fully compatible.

The second oddity of the VIC-20 and Commodore 64 serial port is that it is actually provided by a parallel interface, with built-in software of the computer being used to make certain lines act as serial interface lines. This is of no real practical importance though, and a serial interface implemented in software is not unique to these computers. Using a serial interface is much the same whether it is software or hardware implemented.

Figure 13 provides details of the Commodore quasi RS232C port, which uses several lines of the user port. When operating the user port as a serial interface it is advisable not to have anything else connected to the user port, and any lines used in

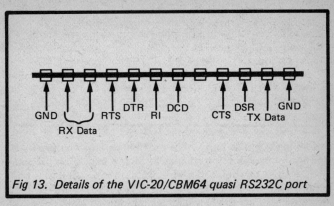

Fig 13. Details of the VIC-20/CBM64 quasi RS232C port

the serial interface should definitely not be connected to any form of peripheral device. Handshake lines as well as the data input and output are included, but there should be no need to connect the handshake lines in this application. It is unlikely that a suitable ready-made connecting lead will be available, and it is a matter of making one up from a couple of 2 by 12 way 0.156 inch female edge connectors and about 2 metres or so of three way cable. The user port connectors of the computers have provision for two polarising keys, and together with matching keys on the female edge connectors these ensure that the sets of connectors can only be fitted together the right way around. Unfortunately, it is unlikely that edge connectors fitted with suitable polarising keys will be available, and it is then a matter of trying to fit suitable keys yourself, or simply marking the top and bottom edges of the female connectors accordingly, so that they are unlikely to be inadvertently fitted the wrong way around.

The advanced manuals for the Commodore 64 and VIC-20 give details of how to use the RS232C port, which is stream 2. A variety of word formats and baud rates can be used. The accompanying listing is suitable for testing the link, and all it does is to print data typed into either computer on the screen of both television sets or monitors. The baud rate is 300 and the word format is 8 data bits,

```
1 REM COMMODORE SERIAL PROG
5 PRINT "": REM CLEAR SCREEN
10 OPEN 2,2,0,CHR$(6)
20 GET#2,A$
30 IF A$ <>"" THEN PRINT A$;
40 GET B$
50 IF B$ <>"" THEN PRINT#2,B$;:PRINT B$;
60 GOTO 20
```

one stop bit, and no parity. The program will run on the VIC-20
and the Commodore 64 computers (or a Commodore 64 compatible type). Of course, if a VIC-20 is used to communicate with
a Commodore 64, allowance has to be made for the fact that the
text screens of the two machines use different formats.

Parallel Interfacing
Connecting two computers via parallel interfaces has disadvantages when compared to the use of serial links, the main one
being that in most cases the link will only be capable of passing
data in one direction. Other drawbacks are the relatively high cost
of the connecting cable, and the limited maximum cable length
that can be used (about 2 metres). The software to handle data
transfers is also likely to be that much more difficult to devise in
most cases, especially if full advantage of a parallel interface's
single plus point is to be achieved. This one advantage is the high
operating speed that can be obtained. The maximum rate at which
data can be transferred depends on the particular hardware used,
and to a greater extent on the software. Using a BASIC routine to
control the system the transfer rate is likely to be no more than
about 100 bytes per second. Using a reasonably efficient machine
code or assembly language routine would boost the transfer rate
by a factor of about one or two thousand times. In other words,
even with a computer having a fairly large RAM capacity of about
128k to 256k, the entire RAM contents could probably be
tranferred from one computer to another in only about one
second. This is about one hundred times faster than a serial

50

interface operating at the maximum standard baud rate of 19200 baud. It has to be admitted that connecting up and using a parallel data link is somewhat more involved than using a serial type, and it is perhaps something which should only be undertaken by reasonably experienced computer users.

It is only possible to implement a parallel link with computers such as the Commodore 64, VIC-20, and BBC model B, which have a user port (or some comparable port). In this context the port is used as a straightforward 8 bit parallel type, with the transmitting computer set up to have eight outputs, and the receiving computer set up to have eight inputs. This basic arrangement is of no practical value since it provides no way for the transmitting computer to indicate to the receiving computer when fresh data is available. This leaves the receiving computer with no reliable way of telling whether or not readings taken from the port are current and valid.

A handshake line must be added so that the transmitting computer can provide a signal immediately after it has placed new data on the eight data lines, to indicate to the receiving computer that new data must be read from the parallel port. This can be accomplished using a strobe output at the transmitting computer which feeds into an edge sensitive input at the receiving terminal. The strobe output simply provides a brief output pulse (typically a few microseconds in duration) after fresh data has been placed on the data lines, and the edge sensitive input then detects this and sets a bit (or "flag") in a register of the parallel interface device. This flag can be monitored by a software loop which prevents data from being read except when a flag-set condition is detected.

It should perhaps be explained that an "edge sensitive" input is one where its static state can not be monitored. Instead, a transition from 0 to 5 volts, or 5 to 0 volts, will set a flag in the register of the interface device. Edge sensitive inputs are of little use for most applications, but are ideal for handshaking applications where it is a transition that is of importance, and not static levels. The main advantage of an edge sensitive input is that it ensures that a strobe pulse, even one lasting only about a millionth of a second, is not missed. The pulse will cause the flag to be set, and the next time the flag is checked the software will detect that it has been set and take the appropriate course of action (which must include resetting the flag). Using an ordinary digital input the state of the strobe line would be periodically checked, but even testing it at one or two hundred thousand times per second a short strobe pulse could occur between checks and be overlooked.

It does not really matter too much whether the strobe pulse is a positive or a negative type, or the type of transition that the handshake input is designed to detect. The strobe pulse will provide both a high-to-low transition and a low-to-high transition, and will therefore activate either type of edge sensitive input. However, the convention is to have a negative strobe output and a handshake input which detects high-to-low transitions (and which therefore detects the leading edge of the strobe pulse). Figure 14 shows how a parallel link can be provided between two user

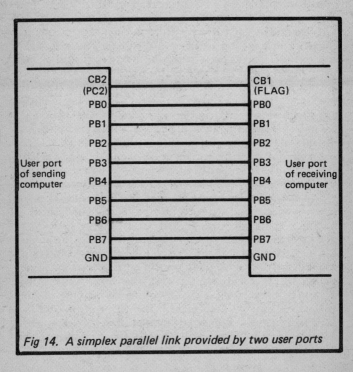

Fig 14. A simplex parallel link provided by two user ports

ports of the type fitted to the VIC-20, Commodore 64, and BBC model B computers. In all three cases the data lines are PB0 (least significant) to PB7 (most significant). For the VIC-20 and BBC model B the handshake output is provide by line CB2, while the handshake input is on CB1. The Commodore 64 has its user port provided by a slightly different device to the one utilized in the other two computers (a 6526 "complex interface adaptor" instead of the more common 6522 "versatile interface adaptor"). This has no exact equivalents to CB1 and CB2, but for our present purposes lines PC2 and FLAG respectively are suitable alternatives.

Wiring the two computers together properly is the first step in effecting a link, and details of the VIC-20, Commodore 64, and BBC model B user ports are shown in Figure 15. The Commodore

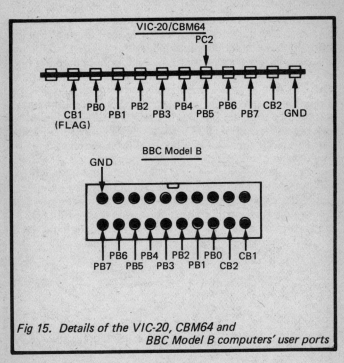

Fig 15. Details of the VIC-20, CBM64 and
BBC Model B computers' user ports

computers use a 2 by 12 way 0.156 inch edge connector, as discussed earlier. The BBC model B computer has a 20 way IDC connector at its user port (on the underside of the machine), and connections to this are made via a 20 way IDC header socket.

Making the connections between the two computers is the easy part, and getting the hardware to provide data transfers is the more tricky business. The computers provide no real aid from their built-in software, and the hardware has to be controlled directly by software routines provided by the user. A basic understanding of the hardware that provides the user ports, or at least the relevant parts of this hardware, is essential if the link is to be of any practical value.

The first task is to set the data lines as outputs on the transmitting computer and as inputs on the receiving computer. The interface device of each computer has a register called the "data direction register", and this is used to control the function of each data line. With the three computers we are concerned with here, writing 0 to a bit of the data direction register sets the corresponding line as an input, and writing 1 to a bit sets the appropriate line as an output. Things are very straightforward in this application where we do not require split operation of the lines, and all eight will be set as inputs on one computer, with all eight set as outputs on the other computer. A value of 0 sets all the lines as inputs – a value of 255 sets them all as outputs. The lines are set as inputs when the computer is first switched on, and this ensures that there is no danger of outputs driving outputs when the two computers are coupled together. While it is not stricly necessary to write a value of 0 to the data direction register of the receiving computer, since its user port data lines will be in the correct mode anyway, it is common practice to do so. This is really done just in case a glitch at switch-on resulted in the lines failing to reset to the input state.

The data direction registers of the three computers are at the addresses listed below:-

CBM64	56579
VIC-20	37138
BBC Model B	&FE62

It is important to realise that the data direction register is only used to set up the user port data lines for the correct type of operation, and is not used when writing data to or reading data from the user port. This is done using the peripheral register, and the addresses of these are listed below:-

CBM64	56577
VIC-20	37136
BBC Model B	&FE60

Some further setting up of the system is required before the link is ready for use. In fact no setting up is required in the case of the Commodore 64 computer, since its PC2 output only functions as a strobe line, and automatically provides a strobe pulse whenever data is written to or read from the user port. Similarly, FLAG only operates as a negative edge sensitive input. The FLAG flag is bit 4 at address 56589, and it is automatically cleared when this register is read.

With the BBC Model B and VIC-20 computers CB1 and CB2 have to be set to the correct operating modes by writing the appropriate value to the Peripheral Control Register at addresses 37148 (VIC-20) and &FE6C (BBC Model B). Bit 4 controls the function of CB1, while bits 5 to 7 control CB2. In this case CB1 is set to the high-to-low transition mode, and CB2 is set to the negative pulse output mode. This requires (decimal) values of 0 and 160 respectively, giving a total value of 160 to be written to the peripheral control register.

The flag for CB1 is at bit 4 of the interrupt flag register at address 37149 (VIC-20) and &FE6D (BBC Model B). This bit can be reset by either writing a 1 to it, or a read or a write operation at the peripheral register. In this application the flag is monitored until it is set, and then the software breaks out of the loop to read the received value at the peripheral register. This effectively gives an automatic clear of the flag.

The accompanying listings give simple test programs for use with the Commodore 64 and VIC-20 computers, and obviously the VIC-20 programs could easily be modified to suit the BBC model B, or any computer which has a user port provided by port B of a 6522 VIA. The Commodore 64 programs will also work with a Commodore computer which has a Commodore 64 compatible mode of operation. The transmitter programs simply transmit any character that is typed into the keyboard, while the receiver programs print any received characters on the screen.

```
5 REM VIC-20 PARALLEL RECEIVER
10 POKE 37138,0
20 POKE 37148,160
30 IF (PEEK(37147) AND 16) = 0 THEN 20
40 A = PEEK(37136)
50 PRINT CHR$(A);
60 GOTO 30


5 REM VIC-20 PARALLEL TRANSMITTER
10 POKE 37138,255
20 POKE 37148,160
30 GET A$
40 IF A$<>"" THEN POKE 37136,ASC(A$)
50 GOTO 30


5 REM CBM64 PARALLEL RECEIVER
10 POKE 57579,0
20 IF (PEEK(56589) AND 16) = 0 THEN 20
30 A = PEEK(56577)
40 PRINT CHR$(A);
50 GOTO 20


5 REM CBM64 PARALLEL TRANSMITTER
10 POKE 56579,255
20 GET A$
30 IF A$<>"" THEN POKE 56577,ASC(A$)
40 GOTO 20
```

All the programs start by setting up the user port for the correct operating mode. The transmitter programs then test to determine whether or not a key has been depressed, and when a key-press is detected the program outputs the character code value to the user port. The programs are looped indefinitely so that any typed characters are transmitted. The receiver programs test to determine whether or not the handshake input flag has been set (using the logic AND function), and when a positive result is obtained the user port is read and the the returned value is converted to a character which is printed on-screen. Again, the program is looped continuously so that any received characters are printed on the screen.

As explained earlier, a parallel link of the type described here can provide data transfers at at high rate, but this requires machine code or assembly language routines. As described here the link does not include a handshake line to permit the receiver to implement a hold-off in the event that data is received at an excessive rate. It would be possible to implement such a link, but it is probably easier to arrange the software so that the transmitter can not output data at an excessive rate, by using NOP instructions or delay loops if necessary.

The user port data lines can be set as inputs or outputs, and there are sufficient handshake lines to permit handshaking in two directions to be provided. Therefore, in theory, it should be possible to implement a half duplex two way link. This would probably not be a good idea though, as there would be a risk of the two ports simultaneously acting as outputs, and possibly causing damage to each other. With computers that have both printer and user ports it might be possible to implement full duplex operation by using the eight data outputs and strobe line of the printer port to transmit data, and utilizing the user port to receive data. The Memotech MTX computers have a user port which provides eight inputs and eight separate outputs, but no handshake lines. It should be possible to implement full duplex operation with these by settling for seven bit data transfers, and using the most significant bit for handshaking purposes. These are only put forward as suggestions for suitably experienced readers who wish to experiment with parallel links, and these ideas have not been tested by the author (although there is no reason in theory why they should not be perfectly feasable).

One final point worth making is that networking is not the only way of tackling things where one printer must be shared between several computers. Selection boxes which enable one parallel printer to be used with several computers (with manual selection) are available. Similar devices for serial interfaces are also available. These do not represent high-tech solutions to peripheral sharing, but are perfectly adequate in most cases, and are likely to be the most cost effective solution.

Chapter 3

RADIO COMMUNICATIONS

Computer communications via radio is potentially the most interesting form of computer communications for the amateur enthusiast, and distances of many thousands of miles can be bridged in this way. In fact radio communications between any two points on the earth is possible, subject to the time of day, the time of year, and other factors providing suitable propogation conditions. However, it only fair to point out right from the start that computer communications via radio links is not something that is as simple as modem communications via the telephone system. For radio communications more complex, more expensive, and more difficult to operate equipment is required, and it is also necessary to have a radio amateurs licence. The latter can only be obtained after passing the radio amateurs examination, and a 12 words per minute morse test as well if operation on the shortwave bands is to be undertaken.

There are plenty of publications which give details of how to obtain a radio amateurs license if you are interested in pursuing this, and it is something that most people could manage provided they have the necessary enthusiasm and are prepared to put a reasonable amount of effort into studying the technicalities. The main purpose of the examination is to ensure that you are able to set up and operate a station competently, without causing radio interference to others (either locally or in the next continent). Things are very much more simple if all you wish to do is operate a receiving station, which is also a very interesting pastime, and one which can be achieved using relatively unsophisticated and inexpensive equipment. Also, no operating licence is required in order to receive amateur radio digital signals.

This is a very technical subject which could easily fill quite a large book on its own. Consequently, here we will only cover the more important technical and practical aspects of computer communications via radio in order to (possibly) whet your appetite, and provide a good idea of just what is involved. It is perhaps worth mentioning that the "Radio Society Of Great

Britain" is the national club for those interested in amateur radio (both licensed amateurs and listeners). Details of how to become a member can be obtained at the address given below. The RSGB can help with details of local radio clubs and courses for those who wish to study for the radio amateurs examination, plus other useful services for those interested in amateur radio.

Membership Services Dept.,
Radio Society Of Great Britain,
Cranbourne Road,
Potters Bar,
Hertfordshire,
EN6 3JW.

FSK

A computer link could be provided between two radio trans-ceivers (transmitter/receivers) capable of handling voice signals simply by using a modem type circuit at each end of the system. In practice this would be a rather overcomplicated way of doing things, and an unnecessarily expensive way of doing things as well. On the other hand, it is not that far removed from the system that has been adopted, and which is known as "frequency shift keying", or "fsk". Some methods of generating fsk signals are in fact essentially the same as using a modem plus a radio voice link, but the standards used in radio links are different to those used in telephone links. Simply coupling a modem to a transceiver would therefore be of little practical value, since there would be no other users operating to the same standards to communicate with.

A basic radio signal just consists of a high frequency carrier-wave. When dealing with the tones in a modem system we are talking in terms of signals which have frequencies of few hundreds of Herts to a couple of kilohertz. In other words, we are sending a few hundred to a few thousand electrical impulses per second down the telephone lines. Radio frequencies are much higher than this, and the shortwave bands are in the frequency range 1.6 to 30MHz (1.6 million to 30 million impulses per second). Most amateur computer radio communications probably take place on the shortwave bands, but it is a form of communications which is equally applicable to the VHF (very high frequency) and UHF (ultra high frequency) bands, where carrier frequencies of hundreds of megahertz may be involved.

Frequency shift keying simply involves switching the carrier between two different frequencies, in much the same way that the audio output from a modem is switched between two frequencies. Also like a modem, one frequency represents the 5 volt (logic 1) level, and the other represents the 0 volt (logic 0) level. The difference between the two systems is that with the fsk system the precise frequencies used are not of importance, but the shift is. The standard frequency shift for amateur fsk links is 170Hz, but shifts of 425Hz and 850Hz are also used in commercial systems.

It would be difficult to devise a circuit that would directly convert the two carrier frequencies to the logic voltages, and this is not the method used in practice. Instead the carrier frequencies are converted to audio frequencies, and they are then demodulated using what is essentially a modem type demodulator circuit. The heterodyning principle is used to bring the two carrier frequencies down into the audio frequency range, and this is achieved using a radio frequency oscillator and a special type of mixer circuit. The mixer combines the fsk input signal and the output of the radio frequency oscillator (which is usually called a Beat Frequency Oscillator or BFO) to produce sum and difference signals. It is the difference signal that gives the required audio frequency output. For example, if the carrier was being switched between 1900kHz (1.9MHz) and 1900.17kHz, a BFO frequency of 1899kHz would give difference frequencies of 1kHz (1900kHZ − 1899kHz=1kHz) and 1.17kHz (1900.17kHz − 1899kHz = 1.17kHz).

In a practical receiver it is unusual for this direct conversion approach to be used, and it is more common for the received signals to be converted first to a fixed "intermediate" frequency band, and then into the audio frequency range using a double heterodyning process. This approach is used in order to give good receiver performance, but whatever type of receiver is utilized, tuning in the signal is much the same. It is a matter of tuning the set to give the correct two audio frequencies for the fsk decoder in use. Assuming the receiver has contiuous tuning, it can be adjusted to produce any two audio frequencies which have the same spacing as the shift of the received signal, but the demodulator will be designed to deal with two particular frequencies. Most decoders have some form of tuning indicator makes accurate tuning perfectly easy, and makes it less of a hit-and-miss affair.

RTTY

Computer communications via a radio link is often called "RTTY", or "radio teletype". This name dates back to the days when communications of this type was carried out using teletype machines that were usually more mechanical than electronic in operation. These are in fact still used to some extent today both in commercial and amateur circles, but they have been largely usurped by computer based equipment. The influence of the old teletype machines is still present though, and this manifests itself in the form of some out-moded methods which are retained in modern RTTY systems. In the fullness of time it is likely that the old system of RTTY communications will be totally replaced by one more appropriate to the computer age, and there are already signs of this happening. However, at the present time the vast majority of digital communications signals on the amateur bands are of the conventional RTTY format.

The most obvious difference between RTTY communications and links using modems is that the ASCII codes are not utilized. The standard RTTY word format is one start bit, 5 data bits, and 1.5 stop bits (2 stop bits are also acceptable, and a single stop bit is normally satifactory in practice as well). Five bit codes are not adequate to handle ASCII codes, and with just 32 codes available, on the face of it there is no way of handling all the letters of the alphabet in both upper and lower case, plus numbers and punctuation marks. In fact five data bits are sufficient to accommodate a usable range of characters, but only by introducing a shift system ("shift" in the sense of a shift key on a typewriter style keyboard) and accepting some limitations.

Each five bit code corresponds to a particular character, but if a shift code is sent, subsequent codes correspond to a different set of characters. The system can be shifted and unshifted at will, effectively doubling the number of codes available (including the shift codes) to sixty four. Many typewriter keyboards have around fifty keys, which gives about one hundred different symbols. These can all be accommodated by the ASCII code set, but a number of characters are not available in the five bit codes. The

61

main characters are included, but one major omission is the full set of lower case letters. The shift system does not use the normal upper/lower case format, but instead operates with an upper case/figures system. The figures set of codes also includes a number of punctuation marks and other symbols. Despite its limitations, this system of coding is adequate for all normal requirements.

This five bit system of coding is called the "Baudot" code, and a full list of the codes is provided below:-

LETTERS	FIGURES	CODE No.
A	—	3
B	?	25
C	:	14
D	$	9
E	3	1
F	%	13
G	&	26
H	½	20
I	8	6
J	'	11
K	(	15
L	)	18
M	.	28
N	,	12
O	9	24
P	0	22
Q	1	23
R	4	10
S	bell	5
T	5	16
U	7	7
V	;	30
W	2	19
X	/	29
Y	6	21
Z	"	17
not used	not used	0
Line Feed	Line Feed	2
Space	Space	4
Return	Return	8
Figures	Figures	27
Letters	Letters	31

There are variations on the figures shift characters, but the letters shift characters are completely standardised. Therefore, if two stations are operating with slightly different Baudot code standards, messages passed from one to the other should not be significantly scrambled. The "bell" code was originally used at the beginning of each message to alert the operator at the receiving station that a new message had commenced. The teletype equipment I have seen operating was noisy to the point where this was of doubtful value, and it is probably not of any use as far as amateur RTTY is concerned, although most computers have a sound generator and could be programmed to give a short beep when the "bell" code is received.

A standard baud rate of 50 is used for commercial RTTY, but some higher rates such as 75 and 110 are also in use these days. The standard baud rate for amateur RTTY in the UK was also 50, but in the USA the standard amateur baud rate was 45.45. Eventually 45.45 baud was agree upon as the universal amateur RTTY standard, and this is the speed that is most likely to be encountered on the amateur bands these days (although some 50 baud RTTY might still be encountered). Of course, only half duplex communication is provided. By using two different transmission frequencies (one to provide communications in each direction) it would in fact be possible to provide full duplex operation, but this system is not used a great deal in practice.

Receivers and Decoders
There are five basic elements to a computer based RTTY receiving station:-

1   The receiver
2   The RTTY decoder
3   The software
4   The computer
5   The monitor

Taking the receiver first, a good quality short wave receiver is ideally what is required. I use a Yaesu FRG8800 which is a micro-processor controlled set which covers all the shortwave bands. Modern sets of this type are very convenient to use, and also have good tuning stability. The latter is important, since any slight drift in the tuning causes the audio output tones to shift, making retuning necessary. Having to almost constantly retune the receiver can become rather tedious, and can also result in much data being lost. A receiver with good tuning stability is a definite asset for this type of reception. Any communications receiver capable of good results is usable though, and an inexpensive secondhand set, provided it is in good working order, should be perfectly suitable. An ordinary broadcast receiver which includes some short wavebands is unlikely to be of much use in this application though. Sensitivity, selectivity, and tuning stability are all likely to be inadequate, and sets of this type do not normally include a suitable reception mode either.

Few communications receivers include a decoded fsk output, and it is therefore necessary to feed the audio output from the headphone or tape socket to an external decoder. Although they are separate parts of the system, the decoder, software, and computer should perhaps be considered as one unit, as it is normally necessary to obtain a decoder and software package to suit the particular computer you wish to use. Some RTTY programs apparently make use of the cassette interface of the computer, with the audio output of the receiver being fed direct into this. Software is then used to provide the decoding. With other systems an external decoder unit is required, and this feeds into a digital input of the computer. Software is then used to decode the serial input signal and provide the display. The second method is the more expensive since a tone decoder is required, but this probably provides superior results with less corruption of data due to noise and interference (although I must admit that I have no experience with systems that dispense with the tone decoder).

The obvious way of providing RTTY reception is to have a decoder to convert the audio tones into logic signals and provide RS232C signal voltages, and to then feed this output to an RS232C or RS423 serial port. This is unlikely to work properly in practice as the chances of the serial port being able to handle any 5 bit word formats is not good, although a few can do so. Even with one that can, there is the problem of the baud rate. Some computers can accommodate 50 baud, but I have yet to come across one that can handle 45.45 baud. This system is therefore only likely to be possible using a custom made serial interface for the computer. In contrast with other systems of RTTY reception, the software would only need to be very simple, with the look- up table method being used to provide the Baudot-to-ASCII conversion.

Many RTTY packages include software and hardware for use when transmitting. It is likely that you will not initially be interested in the transmission side of things, but it does no harm to have the software and hardware available if you should want to use it at some future time. A system for two way communications will not necessarily cost much more than one for reception purposes only. For transmission the function of the system is often to generate Baudot codes from characters entered into the keyboard, and to then convert these (modem fashion) to two audio tones with the appropriate shift frequency. The tones are fed to the microphone input of an SSB transmitter. Although SSB (single sideband) is intended for voice communications, when fed with the audio tones an SSB transmitter gives what is effectively an ordinary fsk output signal. Alternatively the Baudot codes can be converted to a switching action which is then used to drive the fsk input of a transmitter.

Most computers are usable in an RTTY system, but this is not to say that ready-made hardware and software are available for every home computer ever manufactured. If you have a computer which has proved popular over the years and which has a large user-base, then looking through the advertisements in radio and computer magazines should bring a few suitable systems to light. On the other hand, it might not be possible to find a system to suit a computer which has only been in production for a limited period (or was only ever in production for a limited period) no matter how exhaustive the search.

The monitor can simply be the television set or monitor normally used with the computer. However, in any application where a computer is used to display text it is important to have a good quality display if rapid fatigue is to be avoided, and a monitor is preferable to a television set unless the computer concerned is one which gives a very clear and stable display.

Finding RTTY Signals

Having reached the stage where the receiver, aerial, and RTTY receiving terminal are all set up and ready to go, the next step is to find some RTTY to decode. The frequency limits of the six main shortwave amateur bands are given below:-

160 Metres	1.8 to 2.0MHz
80 Metres	3.5 to 3.8MHz (4.0MHz in the USA)
40 Metres	7.0 to 7.1MHz (7.3MHz in the USA)
20 Metres	14.0 to 14.35MHz
15 Metres	21.0 to 21.45MHz
10 Metres	29.0 to 29.7MHz

The amateur bands are split in half, with the lower frequency half being used for CW (Morse Code) and the higher frequency half being used for any mode. It is in fact at roughly the centre of the CW section that most RTTY activity is likely to be found. When initially testing a system the 20 metre band is probably the best one to try, and there are usually a number of strong RTTY signals at around 14.09MHz. This band is virtually useless for local reception, but is excellent for picking up long distance (DX) stations. Any stations you receive are likely to be located hundreds or even thousands of miles away. Conditions on the short wave bands vary according to the time of day, and the 20 metre band often fades out during the hours of darkness, particularly during the winter months. If the 20 metre band has faded, try the 80 metre band at around 3.55 to 3.6MHz. This band gives good medium to long distance reception after dark, as well as local reception both after dark and during the daytime.

You should have no difficulty in picking out RTTY signals from CW and any other signals found on the band, as the warbling sound of the two audio output tones is quite distinctive. The receiver should be switched to an SSB mode, and there is the choice of either upper sideband (USB) or lower sideband (LSB). It does not matter which one you choose, provided the tone decoder has an "invert" switch. If the decoder is giving an output with the logic 1 and logic 0 levels transposed, then the invert switch can be used to correct this. If the tone decoder does not include this facility, then switching from one sideband mode to the other has much the same effect (the lower sideband is the one which will probably give an output signal of the correct polarity). The tone decoder might give some help with indicators to show when everything is tuned and adjusted correctly, and without such indicators RTTY reception becomes very much a matter of trial and error.

With a general coverage (rather than amateur bands only) short wave receiver it is possible to receive a great deal of commercial RTTY, including such things as press reports, weather reports, etc. Be warned though, that reception of many of these stations could be illegal. For instance, reception of news reports would almost certainly represent an infringment of copyright. Much commercial and goverment RTTY is coded these days, and will just produce meaningless five letter groups from an ordinary RTTY receiving station.

CW Systems

RTTY is not the only type of computer communications via a radio link in common use. CW (continuous wave or Morse) is something that can easily be handled by a computer based system. Equipment for both transmission and reception of Morse code are available, or some set ups only provide reception. It is perhaps on the reception side that the use of computers is most useful, as it opens up the world of Morse code to the many shortwave listeners who are unable to read these signals unaided.

The equipment required for Morse reception and decoding is much the same as that needed for RTTY. A receiver, aerial, tone decoder, decoder programme, computer, and monitor are all required. The tone decoder can be somewhat more simple than the type required for RTTY reception, and as with RTTY, sometimes the audio signal is coupled to the cassette interface of the computer with software then being used to provide all the decoding. Whether or not a tone decoder is used, the decoder program is totally different to an RTTY type, and two programs will be needed if you require both types of reception. A RTTY decoder can often be used to decode CW signals incidentally.

Some of the early CW decoders were not paticularly efficient, and had to be set for the particular sending speed in use (Morse speed is specified in words per minute rather than in terms of a baud rate incidentally). These would work well if the received Morse had perfect timing, but Morse code produced by human operators tends to have rather loose timing with the durations of the various elements (dots, dashes, spaces between words, etc.) not strictly adhering to the correct relationships. The software has generally improved as time has passed, and some modern programs can adjust to automatically accommodate any likely sending speed, and they are also more tolerant of slightly less than perfectly formed letter groups.

AMTOR

RTTY is often adequate to provide good reliable contacts, but it is rather crude in many ways, and more sophisticated means of communications are possible using modern computer based systems. AMTOR (Amateur Teletype Over Radio) is an attempt to provide a more reliable system of teletype communications, but it has not received widespread acceptance at the time of writing this. It differs from ordinary RTTY primarily in that it provides a simple system of error correction. In fact there are two operating modes, Mode A (ARQ or Automatic Repeat Request) and Mode B (FEC or Forward Error Correction).

Both systems rely on what is known as "diversity" reception to overcome, or at least to minimise any problems with signal fading or noise. In this case it is time diversity that is used, where characters are sent twice, and at different times. As the two sets of signals are sent at different times they will not be affected by fading or noise in the same way, and there is a good chance that one or other signal will be received properly. The two modes differ in that with Mode A a signal is repeated only when the transmitting station is requested to send a repeat by the receiving station (which must obviously be in two way contact with the sending station). In Mode B every character is sent twice, and this mode is applicable to any receiving station. Mode B is included primarily for use when sending out a call asking for someone to respond and set up a contact (known as sending out a "CQ").

The AMTOR system uses seven bit codes, but these are Baudot rather than (as one might have thought) ASCII based. In other words there are thirty two different codes, including figures and letters shifts, with each Baudot code having a direct AMTOR equivalent. This may seem rather pointless, with the extra two data bits of the AMTOR codes being put to no practical use. In fact the AMTOR codes are arranged so that each one has four bits set to logic 1 and three set to logic 0. This permits a simple but effective form of error checking to be implemented at the receiving station, where any departure from the four 1s and three 0s per character indicates that a character has been corrupted. There are a few spare codes having four 1s and three 0s which are used as control codes (such as "repeat request").

Packet Radio
PSS or Packet Switched Systems were mentioned in Chapter 1, and this is something which is now finding its way into amateur radio. The basic concept is to have a system of repeater stations to provide reliable two way communications over long distances. Repeater stations are by no means a new concept, and have been used with ordinary speech communications, both commercially and in amateur radio, for many years now. The problem with repeaters and analogue communications systems is that any noise and interference received by the repeater station is transmitted together with the wanted signal. With several repeaters strung together the noise can build up to the point where the wanted signal becomes completely swamped and unintelligible.

This can be avoided in digital systems where, provided the received signal can be decoded without errors, it can be regenerated and retransmitted completely free of any noise picked up at the receiver. With a multiple repeater system there is the danger of noise causing serious corruption of data, since a decoding error anywhere in the system will cause an erroneous character to be retransmitted and carried on through the system. With each character being encoded and decoded several times on its way through the link this obviously multiplies the risk of data corruption occuring. This can be combatted using error detection and correction systems though.

One of several major ways in which packet radio differs from ordinary RTTY communications is the use of identification codes for all stations using the system. Users log-on to the network rather like using a database via a modem and the telephone lines. In fact the system could include a database carrying information relevant to amateur radio enthusiasts, and a news page to be sent to users when they log-on. With identification codes information is sent from one user to another specified user of the network. If the intended recipient is not logged-on to the system at the time, then the message could be stored until they do log-on. Again, this is similar to the "mailbox" facility operated by some databases.

The idea of massive systems of this type, for amateur use at any rate, might seem rather far fetched, but in north America the seeds for such a system already exist, and packet radio of sorts is already used by many radio amateurs. Not so many years ago the idea of amateur radio communications satelites would also have seemed rather far fetched, but these have been in existence for several years now, and have been used by substantial numbers of radio amateurs and listeners.

The way in which data is encoded and decoded in a packet radio system is significantly different to that used in RTTY and AMTOR systems, although it is still a form of tone encoded serial data transmission. Perhaps the most radical difference is grouping of bytes into "packets" of data. This differs from sending a group of bytes via an RTTY system in that with an RTTY signal each byte has its own start and stop bits. With packet radio there is effectively a start bit at the beginning of each packet of data, and a stop bit at the end of each packet, with each byte running straight on from the previous one. This helps to give a higher data transfer rate for a given baud rate.

The start and stop bits are actually replaced by bytes of data which are called start and stop "flags". The start flag is also accompanied by one or more bytes giving the address of the sender and the intended recipient, and there may also be some control data. The stop bit is preceded by a number which is calculated by the transmitting station from the bits sent. The receiving station calculates this number from the bits received, and there will be a discrepancy if any data has been corrupted. It is actually possible for the two numbers to match even if data has been corrupted, but the chances of this happening in practice are very remote. This system is much the same as the parity checking system in principle. With parity checking the transmitting station always sends either an odd or an even number of 1s per byte, depending on the type of parity selected. Additional bits are added between the MSBs and the stop bits, where necessary, in order to maintain parity. A simple checking circuit at the receiver tests whether or not an odd or even number of 1s (as appropriate) have been received, and provides a signal of some kind if an error is detected. This system is far from 100% reliable in that a double glitch could easily occur, and could leave the data corrupted but the parity unaltered. The more complex checking system used in packet radio, in effect, does not treat all bits equally, so that corruption of one bit can not easily be balanced by opposite corruption of another bit.

Another difference between RTTY and packet radio is the way in which the digital input signal is converted into serial form. This is not just a matter of having one voltage (and) tone to represent logic 1, and another to represent logic 0. Instead, the NRZI (Non Return to Zero Invert) method has been adopted. With this system a change from one logic level to the other (or one tone to the other) represents a logic 0, while no change in level (or tone) represents a logic 1. Figure 16 might help to clarify this system

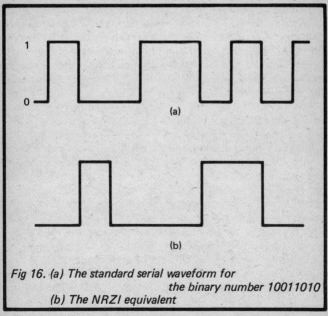

Fig 16. (a) The standard serial waveform for
                                 the binary number 10011010
          (b) The NRZI equivalent

for you. It shows a conventional serial byte and its NRZI equivalent. The NRZI system is apparently less vulnerable to corruption due to noise and fading.

This is only a rather vague description of packet radio, but it should suffice to give a basic understanding of the subject. It is a system which is still under development, and at the time of writing proper standards have yet to be agreed. However, it seems likely that packet radio will play a major role in amateur radio in the future, and it is one of the most exciting aspects of the hobby.